MW00623396

This book contains content about suicide.
If you have thoughts of suicide, please call the National
Suicide Prevention Lifeline at 800-273-8255.

In Deeper

For Nancy

Bethany Lynne Davis

Poland Spring Heritage Days

Writing a memoir is like distilling squid ink—it requires separating truth from facts. Although *In Deeper* is a true story, creative license has been taken with the facts.

Most characters are composites, and names have been changed to protect the privacy of those involved. Dialogue captures the essence of a conversation and should not be taken as a verbatim account of what was said. Compressed or altered chronologies assist the narration. Throughout the pages, emotional truth has been faithfully rendered.

This memoir recounts a difficult time in Beth's life. Those around her experienced events differently, which is their story to tell, not hers.

In Deeper
Copyright © 2021 Bethany Lynne Davis

ISBN: 978-1-63381-292-5

All rights reserved. No part of this book may be reproduced in any form or by any electronic or mechanical means, including information storage and retrieval systems, without permission in writing from the author, except by a reviewer, who may quote brief passages in review.

I would like to express my gratitude to my mentor, Arden Georgi Thompson, who graciously gave me permission to use the poems originally published in her book, Watching Ants.

Cover art used with permission from nomrehsnoom@fountainpen.com

Designed and produced by:
Maine Authors Publishing
12 High Street, Thomaston, Maine
www.maineauthorspublishing.com

Printed in the United States of America

I dedicate this book to my husband, in whom I trust, and my children, in whom I believe.

Table of Contents

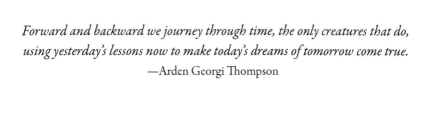

Forward and backward we journey through time, the only creatures that do,
using yesterday's lessons now to make today's dreams of tomorrow come true.
—Arden Georgi Thompson

Tomorrow is never here; only today and endless possibility.
—Arden Georgi Thompson

So It Began

With the end of the school year fast approaching, my seventh-grade classroom filled with students who'd already adopted that air of superiority indicating their ascendance to the top of the pecking order. Five of them waited for the announcement that their bus had arrived.

Devon sidled up to me. "Do you like kids, Mrs. Davis?"

"I'll like them more tomorrow, Dev."

I usually said this in jest.

I'd be sorry to see Devon move on to eighth grade come June. A goofy grin was always glued to his freckled face, replete with dimples and a cleft chin, which chimed with his personality. He investigated the world through touch; his elvish fingers explored objects as if reading Braille. His self-effacing honesty earned my trust. He was developing into a gentle young man, wise and kind and funny.

Devon thrived in my science class, where success didn't depend upon reading and writing. He didn't think of himself as the gifted student he was. Dyslexic, he could describe black holes as lively and ordered parts of the universe but couldn't spell gravity. Some defined him by his learning disability rather than his knowledge and bright personality. All I saw was a special human being.

His look always featured skinny jeans, pressed Oxford button-front shirts, and penny loafers with no socks. I wished I could vanquish the bullies who teased him. Instead, I was just a teacher who had never learned how to change their attitudes.

1

In the back of my classroom, more than 200 Madagascar hissing cockroaches hid in the nooks and crannies of paper towel tubes stacked inside a fifty-five-gallon aquarium. Devon devoted himself to their care and caressed their chitin-covered bodies as if they were little gerbils. He hid bits of banana and cantaloupe in the aquarium and changed their water containers every day before dismissal.

I joined Devon at the aquarium, and we dismantled the cockroach condominiums together, then rebuilt them with fresh paper towel tubes.

"Oh, cool! Mrs. Davis, look! One's molting!"

His exclamation brought students who usually treated the insects like creepy-crawlies to witness the miraculous event. A girl asked if she could hold the snow-white creature who had shrugged halfway out of his exoskeleton.

Devon advocated for the beastie. "No, you'd hurt him."

Craig, an arrogant, pretentious boy, spoke up. "Ha! Him? How do you know it's a him? Been watching the buggers bugger?"

I was furious at the innuendo. "Craig, have a seat until the bus comes. You've got a morning detention with me—we'll talk then."

I knew from past battles that Craig's parents would consider the remark funny. By their standard, making an insinuation about Devon being gay was something their son would never do. There'd be no formal response from the administration either, but making Craig miss a block of time he usually spent with his buddies was a comeuppance I could control.

The intercom intruded. "Third run of buses."

Craig glared at me as he exited the classroom. The room emptied, except for Devon, who carefully arranged cardboard around the vulnerable insect.

"I'll finish, Dev. Go ahead so you don't miss your bus." I fiddled with the water dishes and slid the mesh cover into place.

Within, a black mood warred. I needed to be at a teachers' meeting in a half-hour with my assignment in hand. The bulletin read: *Please prepare a synopsis of your teaching framework, beliefs, and practices to present at tomorrow's meeting.* The useless chore frustrated me. Throughout my twenty-four-year career, I'd met the national learning standards by implementing engaging lessons and assessed knowledge by analyzing students' next best questions rather than their answers. Instead of using disciplinary programs, I cultivated genuine relationships with my students.

What interested me about teaching was students' thought processes. My newest mentor was Dr. Derek Cabrera, a Cornell University professor. He had identified the brain's four essential patterns of thinking: making distinctions, finding parts and wholes, analyzing relationships, and adopting new perspectives. He was an international expert in his field, and I followed him like a disciple, captivated and intrigued by the possibility of conversing with students' ideas before, during, and after their construction.

On this day, I intended to share Dr. Cabrera's research instead of my methodology during the meeting. I planned to introduce an alternative topic to discuss: the difference between gaining information and building knowledge. Exhilaration extinguished my frustration, and a subdued sort of frenzy fueled my need to put forth my agenda.

In the library, Mr. Clark, the principal, climbed onto a table. It was a move designed to grab an audience's attention, which he'd learned from me. "Listen up, my friends." He jumped to the floor, and I was relieved he landed upright as both he and I were old enough to know bounding off a table was ill-advised. "Once you form groups, you have my permission to take your conversations anywhere." He bowed to his audience.

My peers cheered and gathered into cliques. I heard talk about pubs and hanging out by a pool. Any place was better than having to conference in the stuffy library.

It had happened again; I was the outlier without a group to call my own. No one was to blame. I didn't frequent the staff room enough to be included in the social magic that brings people together.

A job posting for a fourth-grade position thumbtacked to the staff room's bulletin board captured my attention. Grandiose dreams of working in a different school sang a siren's song. Should I pursue it? The fact that I would lose my tenure as lead science teacher at the middle school didn't occur to me. Checking in with friends or consulting my husband never entered my mind.

Enchantments should never be broken.

The groups had scattered to the four winds. Who would know which one I'd chosen to join? I escaped to my room and caught Craig nosing around the back shelves. At first, I was surprised, then nervous, wondering how and why he'd entered my classroom.

Craig, ever the quick thinker, covered his tracks. "I forgot my charger. Do you have it?"

"I'll be sure to look. How did you get in?" I escorted him toward the door. "You know what? I don't want to know. I'll see you in the morning, and we'll talk then."

He'd missed the bus, so I marched him to the office. The secretary could call his parents or permit him to walk home; I didn't care which.

During the walk back to my room, I made a quicksilver decision to write an email to the superintendent of schools to ask for the fourth-grade position. I reasoned that elementary-aged students would be too young to know what an innuendo was. Besides, closing my career in a new classroom seemed like a fun thing to do.

If I'd had a balcony to observe myself as a player on the stage, I might have recognized the seriousness of my circumstances. Instead, I was the center of the universe and didn't wobble. From my perspective, I was stable, and it was the external world's chaos that forced me to respond to its problems.[1]

---

1. This lack of insight was called anosognosia; it was not that I denied I was ill, but that I was unaware.

To: Mark Hughes, Superintendent
From: Bethany Davis, Grade 7
Subject: 4th Grade Position

Dear Mark,
    Noticed fourth-grade job posting at Jefferson. Any chance I can have it?
    Beth

Immediately, I wished I hadn't sent it. Surely, I thought, the universe would recognize my missive as a regrettable dare. Then, the madness took hold again. I slyly smiled and decided I'd let Mr. Hughes' decision determine my fate. I didn't want to withdraw my query—he might think me crazy.

To: Bethany Davis, Grade 7
From: Mark Hughes, Superintendent
Subject: Re: 4th Grade Position

Sure, stop by Central Office and do the paperwork.
    Mark

I'd rubbed the djinn's magic lamp and gotten my wish. Instead of joining a group to discuss my practice, I drove to Central Office and signed a new contract accepting the position at Jefferson Elementary, a K–4 school in a neighboring town within our district. My inner voice yelled and warned me not to do it, but I ignored my premonition.

The following day, I arrived at school early to prepare my lessons before Craig's arrival. My key slid into the lock in the usual way, but when I opened the door, I heard a scuttling noise as if someone stood near sweeping with a bristle broom.

I flicked on the lights. The swish turned into rustling. Then, the room returned to its usual stillness.

A ghost? There were rumors of one that dwelled in the boiler room. Mice? The noise was too loud for it to have been a few little rodents scurrying about the place.

What was the aquarium's mesh lid doing in the corner of the room? Behind the aquarium's glass, blackened banana bits and slimy cantaloupe pieces dotted the empty cardboard tubes. Not a creature stirred. Even the little guy who had shed his skin was gone.

Ah, this was what Craig had been up to—the cockroaches! They'd had all night to crawl forth. The runaways could have made it down the hallway to the locker rooms, the principal's office, *the cafeteria*!

I fled down the hall on the pretext of getting some milk for my coffee which I always drank black. The cafeteria ladies were calm and good-natured about my request—a good sign. There'd have been a kerfuffle had they discovered black, thumb-sized crawling critters.

Back in my classroom, I heard the rustle again. It came from my drawers. I opened them expecting to find a milling horde, but everything was in place. A second shuffling noise made me look underneath the drawer's bottom. A coating of cockroaches clung, upsidedown, to the drawer's bottom, a living veneer of rustling creatures.

I collected a handful, lowered them into the aquarium, replaced the lid, and then returned for more.

Craig arrived and gave me a sullen look.

I was pleased. He'd have to right his wrong.

Neither of us said a word.

For the duration of his morning detention, we hunted for insects. They had crawled between the pages of books, behind framed posters, and sandwiched themselves between the paper and cork of the bulletin board. They found their way inside cupboards and crawled into computer cases.

Craig and I searched every nook and cranny, every envelope, and between loose papers. He didn't enjoy the roundup, but I did.

I imagined the James Bond theme music playing during the great escape of the clever creatures. What a night they must have had!

A knock on the door—it was Mr. Clark.

I surveyed the surfaces in my room and motioned to Craig. "Put the cover on the aquarium; then you can go."

Mr. Clark's usually jovial face was stern, his mouth tight. I was sure he'd discovered I hadn't met with a group to discuss my teaching framework. He had me dead to rights.

He thrust his coffee mug toward me. "Mrs. Davis, do these belong to you?" Inside were two large Madagascar hissing cockroaches.

"Yes." I couldn't lie, as I was the only teacher in the district who kept the damned things in an aquarium. I wanted to know where he'd found them as I was sure there were more and wanted to sequester them before they were discovered by others.

His eyebrows narrowed. "Is there something I should know?"

"Nope."

I didn't want to discuss the escapees,[2] Craig, my whereabouts, or my new position.

---

2. Only three other cockroaches were discovered outside my room—one under the bleachers in the gym and a little guy who thought hiding in the Lost and Found was ironic. I found one months later inside the glove box of my car. I don't know if any others ventured outside the school building, but fortunately (or unfortunately, depending upon your perspective), Madagascar hissing cockroaches can't live through snowy winters.

I wonder if a snail knows it wears a shell.
I didn't until I broke, and it fell.
—Arden Georgi Thompson

The Snail

I was terrified of starting fourth grade at Jefferson Elementary. Nothing seemed odd about severing my ties and flouncing off to a new school. I felt as if I stood on a roller coaster poised at the brink of falling into a death dive, confident I'd survive and laugh at those too cowardly to join me. A rapturous logic held sway. That my changing mood was linked to menopause was inconceivable. I was fifty-five and believed I was at the zenith of my career.

At the same time, my gut recognized I was a zebra on the run from a lion.

The only reason I had come to school on that oppressive August day was to meet Brian, but he wouldn't enter the building. I occupied my time designing cute name tags for my students' desks. His two-inch-thick folder lay beneath the scraps. It held documents that gave me all the information I needed: Brian had been identified as being on the spectrum.

From the teacher's desk in my new classroom, I watched out the window as the ten-year-old twisted a playground swing into a cyclone of brown-haired child and chain. His mother, a beautiful, ample woman in her mid-forties, lolled on the shaded grass, one knee drawn up and clasped by her hands. I thought she was remiss in allowing such behavior, but it was none of my business.

Brian's family had moved from a small city to our rural school district. Before the family left their hometown, a team of teachers had recommended Brian be placed in a regular classroom and receive support from special education services.

Mine was to be the *regular* classroom.

Changing schools was challenging for any child, but it would be especially tricky for Brian. I had no idea how to help. Not once in my career had there been a workshop about dealing with students on the autism spectrum. At the middle school, special education teachers and aides provided support, but that role now fell to me. How could I help a fourth grader with compromised social skills integrate into a foreign classroom filled with aliens? This was a problem I'd never encountered.

Brian's mother rose from the grass. As the spinning swing lost its momentum, she hunkered down and reached a hand toward the boy. Her thick dark hair tumbled opulently down her back, reminiscent of an Alphonse Mucha art nouveau painting. Graceful. Serene. There was no trace of annoyance about her; she simply waited and allowed Brian to decide on entering the building.

Their conversation didn't carry through the glass. I watched Brian recoil from his mother's touch. He heaved his backpack from the ground and trudged to their car. His mother followed.

They left more familiar to me, yet still strangers.

The first day of school fell on a Thursday. Twelve long-stemmed red roses sent by my husband, Joel, sat in the middle of my desk. It never mattered how long I fussed with preparations; the hours before students arrived were always filled with last-minute tasks. The principal had added a new student to my roster, so I needed to make another name tag, request a workbook, and make room for another desk. More urgently, I needed to complete my bus list.

A teacher's bus list verified the accuracy of the transportation department's records. Boarding three hundred children, half of whom couldn't read, onto the correct yellow bus—which, to their eyes, looked like every other bus—presented a herculean challenge.

At the middle school, dismissal required no explanation; students were experts at evacuating the building. At Jefferson Elementary, though, any glitch caused a ripple in the transportation system's complicated schedule, which moved three thousand children across twenty-five hundred miles of roads twice a day.

Engrossed in cross-checking information on forms with computer records, I didn't notice Brian's mom until she knocked at my door. I motioned her to enter and smiled, even though I secretly wished she'd go away and leave me to my work.

"You don't mind if I interrupt, do you?" The two cups of coffee and the bakery bag she carried made it clear I had no choice.

"Of course not; I'm glad you're here." What else do you say to a concerned mom? I set aside the task of finishing my bus list, accepted the coffee, and gave in to the doughnut. After engaging in small talk, we stepped into the hall.

Brian waited near the end of the corridor. He repeatedly flung his heavy backpack so high it hit the ceiling, then he let it slide through his hands as it fell to the floor. Thunk, swish, thunk. Thunk, swish, thunk.

"Sorry about not making it into the building last week." Brian's mother kept a steady bead on me while backing toward her son. "There've been too many new things, and he was overwhelmed. He's very excited to get started, though."

She neared Brian, who again smacked the ceiling with his pack, only to let it fall. Her foot trapped the strap, then she slid it across the floor toward my door and turned to look at her son. "Time to get settled."

Brian panicked and plastered himself against the wall like a human snail. He slid toward the classroom, rasping his shirt against the cinder blocks. By the time he neared my door, sweat dripped down his temple.

Brian's mom smiled with amusement, but her voice remained assertive. "Keep it going, bud. We haven't got all day."

The snail reached the classroom door. Brian adopted a dramatic put-upon pout, heaved his pack from the floor, and shouldered it across the threshold. The drama ended when he saw my framed poster of the Periodic Table of Elements above the coat hooks.

"I know that!" He turned to me. "Ag is gold, and Au is silver." His backpack fell away as the snail jettisoned its shell.

Brian's mother transferred one new pencil, one eraser, and one box of markers from the backpack into his desk, pocketing the Matchbox cars and LEGOs with practiced deftness. Her sparkling eyes found mine, and she patted her pocket. "Pick your battles."

She spoke over her shoulder to her son, still preoccupied with the poster. "Bri, I'm taking your books back home, so you have room for your lunch box."

Another cunning move.

Brian edged toward his mother. "Did you do two?"

"Yup. It's the second day of September, so you have two cherry tomatoes."

When my children were his age, they'd have required a ten-dollar bill to elicit such joy. Strangely, I understood the pleasure of having two items on the second day of the month.

The three of us left my classroom to join the other children on the playground, the nearly finished bus list forgotten on my desk. After the first bell, Brian's mother headed for her car while my class and I found our way to Room 403.

Students sifted and sorted their new school supplies into their desks, checked out their cubbies, and chattered as they made new friends. I ignored the controlled chaos because a note written with a red marker lay on my computer: *I need your bus list.* The principal had underlined the word "need" twice.

Brian found himself in dire straits as well. Twice the size of his peers, he couldn't fit under his desk. I watched in consternation as the child flipped the desk onto its side so hard it bounced.

The other students and I froze in place. Pick my battle, indeed. I chose to ignore the desk and concentrate on making peace.

No Allen wrench in the world could make that desk high enough for Brian. I set the note aside, motioned to my desk, and mouthed the words, "Just for today." The crisis may as well have never happened; he snapped from catastrophe to calm.

Brian settled himself at my desk.

The rest of us resumed our activities as if the event had never happened.

The intercom interrupted: "Mrs. Davis, send a student with your bus list to the office. Now."

～

A lull in the noise cued me that it was time to cast the magic spell that would meld strangers into a class. I pulled a balloon from my pocket, stretched it, and began my introduction. "My name is Mrs. Davis, and I'm nervous because I'm new to this school."

A pixie of a girl rested her head on her hand. "I know how you feel, I'm new too."

I thought it odd I didn't know her name; usually, they stuck the first time I read through my roster. "We'll help each other, okay?" I glanced at Brian, seeking an opportunity to include him, but he was engrossed in reading the teacher's manual for our math program.

I made a show of blowing up the balloon. "Whoa! I thought it'd pop for sure!"

Students with hands over their ears or eyes squeezed shut indicated they did too. I tied off the end and glanced at a name tag on a nearby desk. "Katie, do you see the bamboo skewer on the shelf? Bring it to me, would you?"

I slid the skewer I had soaked in vegetable oil through the tied end of the balloon. Students ducked, gasped, or pulled back into their chairs as far as they could.

"A few of you recognized me." I fiddled with the skewer until it exited through the balloon's dimpled end. "Have you figured out where you know me from?"

No one cared; all eyes were on the unexpected event: an impaled balloon. "You may have met me during Open House at the middle school."

"That's it! That's where I saw you!"

The class regarded me as if I were of a different ilk. After all, most teachers didn't play with balloons on the first day—plus, I kept company with the big kids, the bane of their existence.

Sloane asked, "Are you the one that had them cockroaches?"

"I am. Lots of them."

An impish grin broke out under his broad nose. "My brother said they got loose."

"That they did." I sized up Sloane.

A knock on the door interrupted my thoughts about the night of the great escape.

The lady from the cafeteria poked her head into the room. "Your lunch count is late."

No one told me about lunch counts. At the middle school, students handled such details.

Sloane rose to get a paper slip. "Don't worry, Mrs. Davis; I can do it for you."

We reached that indefinable point when individual identities merged into one; we became a class: Room 403. I began my first formal lesson by projecting M. C. Escher's *Waterfall* on the screen. The impossible figure depicted a mill powered by the cascading water that churned into a stream that meandered back up to the mill.

I waited for a student to ask a question or make a remark. My fourth-graders sat silently. I knew these children had minds as capable as those of middle schoolers. Could I be wrong? The real problem registered: these kids were well trained. I held the ball but hadn't served the question; they waited for me. "This year, we aren't going to raise our hands."

The children raised their hands to ask me questions about raising their hands, wiggling their bodies across the surface of their desks like prairie dogs creeping out of burrows.

I contradicted myself and called on Amanda.

"You're gonna to get in trouble from the principal. You gotta raise your hand in school."

Laurie couldn't contain herself. "How are you gonna know who's right if you don't call on us?"

Brian noticed the water climbed and descended simultaneously. "Wait! That doesn't work!"

"Show us." I turned the stage over to Brian by walking toward the back of the room.

The intercom squawked. "Bus rehearsal will begin at ten."

Brian bellowed at the intercom. "It's my turn! You aren't supposed to interrupt people." Then, he tucked his shirt back into his pants and smiled angelically. "Excuse me. That was impolite."

I wondered if he meant his behavior was discourteous or if the principal who spoke over the intercom without excusing himself were the problem.

It was time to line up. Brian investigated the schedule instead. "Excuse me, Mrs. Davis, you made a mistake; reading should be in the afternoon. I'm not allowed to read a book before lunch." His eyes traveled down the schedule. "No! It can't be! Lunch is at eleven forty-five? Oh, no. I'll starve!" His attention shifted to the list of reading and math groups taped to the wall. "I can't be in the orange group. I don't like orange."

The intercom buzzed. "All classrooms should be outside."

Brian's eyebrows almost collided, his brown eyes squinched, and shoulders hunched. He took three deep breaths and then politely interrupted. "Excuse me, Mrs. Davis; he didn't say excuse me again."

Once we had arrived at our crack in the sidewalk, Brian and I stood together, transfixed by so many bodies in motion. Each bus pulled up to the school, and students practiced climbing aboard. Then, the bus drove around the circular drive, and the students disembarked.

"Where's my bus?" Brian rode the van that shuttled students with special needs back and forth; apparently those kids didn't get to practice.

I'd missed that detail and explained he was already good at it. The platitude didn't fix the fact he was an outlier.

Returning to the classroom, we passed the lunch ladies who stood in the hall with their hands on their hips, scowling at me. I smiled back, hoping to relieve the tension. I underestimated the clockwork precision of Jefferson Elementary School's routines. My tardiness to bus practice had dominoed into their domain.

In my new setting, one-fifth of the school's population had never been in a cafeteria before. Kindergartners were too short to reach the lunch counter, so they slid the trays toward themselves at eye height without knowing how to position their little fingers to keep their forks and spoons in the side slot. They spilled their trays while trying to glimpse their lunch or bending to pick up a fallen straw. The fold-down table benches required them to make a physical ascent to sit on them, a challenge when carrying a large tray.

One of the lunch ladies shrugged her shoulders when Room 403 lined up last at the serving window. "We're out of corn. It's getting late, you know."

I didn't think it would be too difficult to heat another can and said so.

The cafeteria ladies let me know that was an unthinkable solution. They'd have to report the discrepancy to their supervisor. I couldn't reconcile their point of view with mine and knew better than to argue with a system I knew nothing about.

I fled to the office. The teacher who taught in the classroom across the hall, Mrs. Westcott, entered and grabbed a stack of notes from her mailbox. "Come join us for lunch!"

"No." Overwhelmed and overstimulated, I forced my face to polite neutrality. I hadn't eaten lunch in the teachers' room at the middle school, where I knew and liked everyone. The very thought of eating with strangers conjured up the dark heart of a fairy tale. My feeling of otherness prevailed; past experience warned that I wouldn't fit in. I decided to boycott the teachers' room in its entirety.

With no more evidence than the flick of Mrs. Westcott's ponytail and the way she bobbed down the stairs toward the staff room, I decided she was judgmental and dismissive. From her perspective, she probably didn't notice my hesitancy. From mine, there were too many unknowns. A dash of paranoia had surfaced.

After lunch, it was time for the second bus practice. I noticed Brian wasn't at his desk. "Where's Brian?"

The girl with the frizzy hair raised her hand. "The cafeteria ladies let him go to the bathroom."

After finding Brian twirling outside the library, I frowned at the lunch ladies as we passed. They had allowed him to leave their territory unsupervised, and now I would arrive late at our crack in the sidewalk again.

They smiled back.

We lined up once more before trekking outside. Brian lagged, having resumed being the snail. He kept full-body contact with the wall all the way, sliding to the front doors of the building.

Thinking to shepherd him back to the line, I remembered his mother's wise directive: pick your battles. I let him find his way in his peculiar manner, a choice that caused near-by teachers to raise their eyebrows.

After the final bus practice of the day, Room 403 filled with grumpy, tired children. My favorite book from when I was a fourth-grader, *The Borrowers* by Mary Norton, sat like a life jacket to the left of the open window. I turned off the lights, then leaned against the top of a low bookcase. I read from the book's first page: Mrs. May first told me about them.

I paused to let the children relax and resettle into their chairs.

The intercom squawked. "Dismissal will begin in five minutes. Teachers, be sure students take their notes home. Thank you."

I should have checked my mailbox. I considered breaking the cardinal rule of never leaving your classroom to get mine. If I asked nicely, Mrs. Westcott might have watched Room 403, but I had been rude by refusing her invitation to lunch, so I thought it best to avoid that choice.

Brian tugged on my arm. "Excuse me, Mrs. Davis, he did it again. You have to say excuse me; it's a rule."

The principal knocked on my door, handed me the notes that needed to go home, then turned on his heel and walked away.

I was too grateful and tired to feel embarrassed. "Thank you!"

He flicked his hand in a bit of a wave over his shoulder and spoke into the air. "Look in your mailbox for an updated bus list. Double-check the changes and get it back to me."

Brian's eyes opened wide. He had recognized his voice. "Mrs. Davis, that's him! Can I tell him about saying excuse me?"

I smiled. "I think that would be very nice. Be sure to tell him to have a nice day too."

What was it about this child? Rather than evaluating his behavior and correcting him, my perspective centered inside his body. I watched the world through his eyes. What made him twirl in front of the library? I thought it was the comforting presence of books lined up on the shelves in the same predictable pattern of his old school.

Brian needed black-and-white rules and shared my discomfort with the color orange. I'd crawled inside his shell and intuitively sensed the wellspring of his actions. He was familiarly strange.

I will give you who I am, if you'll not fear or envy me.
How others see us either holds us captive or sets us free.
—Arden Georgi Thompson

The Shunning

As the weeks passed, school days grew more and more difficult for Brian and me. Disruptions to our daily routine happened frequently, and each one required that I manage not only the emerging circumstances with other students but also Brian's distress. Each change loosened his tenuous grip on a slippery slope.

At first, he sobbed, but over time the sobs gave way to screams. It tortured him every time I announced a school assembly, that the guidance counselor would pop in for a lesson, or that we'd play a math game before recess.

One day in October, I reoriented Brian to the flabbergasting truth that reading, not math, happened in the morning as it had each day since the first day of school. "Bri—it's your turn at the listening station."

He whined he'd get in trouble if I didn't allow him to finish his math homework assignment first, an avoidance strategy.

"We'll figure math out after lunch. Yesterday, you chose the story about Jackie Robinson. You may listen to it at your desk or near the coat closet."

Brian carried the tape recorder to the corner of the classroom and snapped the cassette into place. He put the headphones on upside-down, so the head strap hung below his chin like a football player with half a helmet, pressed play, and closed his eyes.

I sat on the cold tile floor on the other side of the room from him. My attention focused on a small group of children who struggled with a vocabulary game.

Brian exploded out of the corner, screaming as if he'd disturbed a ground nest of yellow jackets. He flung aside the headphones, which landed squarely on Greg's head, making him howl too.

Brian escaped to the hall.

I dashed across the room, sliding between desks and stepping around chairs left askew in the aisles to investigate Greg's injury. Already swollen, his wound warranted a precautionary trip to the nurse.

I shepherded Greg in front of me and peeked into the hall, expecting to see Brian wilted in a corner, but there was no hint of his whereabouts. In need of help, I knocked on Mrs. Westcott's door and asked her to watch my class. After leaving Greg in the secretary's care, I chased a shadow I couldn't see.

Brian had vanished.

The principal, Mr. Blanchard, noticed the ruckus, and immediately launched a search party after I explained the situation. Within minutes, the janitor found him outside, sandwiched between the bushes and the school's exterior bricks.

The janitor escorted Brian through the front entrance. A chilly breeze had evaporated the sweat from his brow, leaving salted tendrils plastered across his forehead. The nurse wrapped him in a blanket. Knowing he was safe, I returned to my classroom.

The lunch bell set the school in motion. Before the last child was seated in the cafeteria, I left to talk to Brian.

He paced to the side of the office's glass door, waiting for his mother. A blanket clutched around his shoulders swaddled his anxiety. "What's up, Bri?" I brushed a stiff curl from his eyebrow. My touch triggered tears. "You don't need to tell me, but you'll need to apologize to Greg because throwing the tape recorder hurt him."

Tears turned to heaving sobs.

Intuition suggested I leave the matter alone, so I turned my attention to the incident report already waiting in my mailbox. I pulled a chair to a nearby table. The form's first field required me to identify the apparent cause of the incident.

Brian crept up behind me, a ghost under a fleece blanket. "I got scared."

Ah, this great escape was nothing more than a startled fourth-grade boy running from a sound effect: the crack of Jackie Robinson's bat. Like a fly trying to escape a spider's web, he entangled himself in the school's disciplinary system.

Mr. Blanchard decided Brian would lose his recess privileges for two days due to harming a fellow student and leaving the building without permission. It was a sorrowful loss for an unintended action.

In the classroom, the students' collective gavel fell. They found him guilty of being weird. I recognized ostracism's quicksand but couldn't pull him to safety.

Brian tried to repair his relationship with Greg. "You can have cuts in line."

Greg stayed where he was.

"I'll carry your backpack."

Greg got huffy. "Don't touch my stuff."

Brian's attempts at atonement failed. He would always be a member of Room 403, but he'd stand apart from the other children, ever hopeful the distance might be permeable.

By early November, I didn't care who knew how badly I needed help. I requested an Individualized Education Plan (IEP) meeting with other professionals in the school district to discuss Brian's ongoing struggle.

"I don't understand." The behavioral specialist drummed a pencil on the papers in front of her. "He seems to be doing so well."

"That's because I've become his one-on-one aide. I can't do that and support the other three who qualify for special services. And let's not forget the sixteen kiddos waiting for their teacher to peek at their work."

"It's okay. We like what you're doing."

The guidance counselor nodded in agreement.

Mr. Blanchard had paperwork in front of him. "Brian's previous school indicates he was ready to be included in a regular classroom. Let's give the transition more time."

I sagged in my chair.

One day, while sitting at my desk eating during my twenty-minute lunch break, Mr. Blanchard interrupted. "Excuse me, Mrs. Davis, would you join me in the cafeteria?"

Who needed to eat?

Brian had dilly-dallied on his way to the cafeteria. He may have been distracted by the stair railing's metallic luster, or perhaps he'd listened to the whispers of tissue paper lanterns hung from the ceiling. Whatever the diversion, Brian had missed the distribution of extra chocolate pudding.

We found him sprawled on the cafeteria's cold tile floor. A Shakespearian actor had possessed his body, and he behaved as if the shores of Hades loomed on the horizon. Random sniffles interrupted his tragic soliloquy. "I hate you. You said I was too late, and I wasn't even late—I was almost getting here. Everyone else got to have extra pudding, but you couldn't wait until I got ready. I didn't even know I had to get ready because no one told me to get ready. It's not fair!" He repeated his grievances, using the same phrases repeatedly as he rocked his head from side to side in despair and protest.

I watched his performance, wondering why the guidance counselor or behavioral specialist weren't involved. What made their lunch sacrosanct, but not mine?

Mr. Blanchard and I sat at a nearby table to wait until Brian's energy dissipated. The students had returned to their conversations.

The cafeteria ladies scowled at me as if I caused the situation.

I left the table. "Brian, will you eat here or in the classroom?"

"I'll stay here." He climbed to his feet and wiped his eyes with his left sleeve and nose with his right.

Mr. Blanchard's forehead arched.

I was just as astonished and hoped he thought Brian's remarkable turnabout was due to my expertise. I put my hand on Brian's shoulder. "I'd have been disappointed too."

A third-grade girl brought her extra pudding and set it in front of Brian. His every muscle vibrated; he clenched his jaw and growled, then picked up the plastic cup and chucked it against the wall with fury. Chocolate pudding splattered across the wall's expanse, then rained upon nearby students. The little girl cowered behind me.

Brian turned, moved around me, and yelled in her face. "I just got controlled. I was gonna be okay. Now, what'd you do that for when I was just getting controlled?"

He had weathered the lack of pudding but couldn't handle generosity. Brian seldom experienced genuine tenderness from his peers and couldn't tolerate the flood of emotions unleashed by the random act of kindness.

Mr. Blanchard called his mother, who took Brian home to calm down and pull himself together for another day.

I spent the rest of my lunch chatting with the third-grade girls about how taking the right action can sometimes cause unexpected problems and assured them the way Brian reacted didn't sully their generosity.

⁂

Brian's inner world was unfathomable to most. Each day, his behavior disintegrated into a problem. He was a jack-in-the-box with no lid to close or handle to turn. Each day, he popped.

Earnest and fierce, Brian's heart never hid behind pretense. Every morning, a joyful, exuberant child crossed the threshold. At some random time, fear caused him to run like a prey animal, or anger unleashed his fury. To his credit, he never hurt anyone except Greg, but he slammed doors so hard framed posters fell from cinder block walls. Room 403's collective psyche became wary of Brian.

The most recognizable problem was the hardest to solve. The difficulty didn't come from fear, anger, temper tantrums, or social stressors. Brian experienced meltdowns.

Meltdowns happened when incoming sensory information exceeded his brain's ability to process it. The classroom was the opposite of a sensory deprivation tank: clocks ticked, people coughed, and doors snicked open and closed. Fabric touched his skin, wet coats smelled, and pencils got sharpened. Air currents whispered; fluorescent lights buzzed. Colors vied for attention, and orange irritated. At any random moment, Brian's brain signaled enough was enough.

Like a computer running amok, he needed to shut down before rebooting. He calmed himself by spinning a button on a string, rocking forward and back, and squeezing his eyes open and shut so hard I imagined his eyeballs popping in protest.

Brian's shut-down process needed to reach its inevitable conclusion: a return to normalcy. The classroom provided no soft landing pad that would afford him the dignity and privacy he required to collect himself. We relied upon the quiet, cluttered, stinky coat closet to work as his bear's den.

Structures in Brian's brain created a different interface with the world. Sounds, colors, people's expressions, and speech intonations impacted him in the same way walking through a fun house at a local fair might keep anyone on high alert. The ordinary remained extraordinary to him all the time; he didn't acclimate or "get used" to things. When he reached his limit, his brain signaled its distress.

Brian cared about his behavior. He wanted to do well, but he had needs neither the coat closet nor I could meet. He apologized each time his behavior strayed, and by accepting them, I implied his apologies were appropriate.

One day, the gym teacher crossed her arms when I escorted Room 403 to her class. "Brian seems to be in such a bad mood today." She looked me in the eye. "Maybe he should stay with you."

I bit my tongue and didn't counter that she was his teacher too. It was unprofessional to argue in the hall in front of students. Stupid woman. He wasn't moody; he was on the verge of a meltdown but had to go to PE class. The echo chamber called a gym throbbed with pounding balls, and it was a place where a teacher bellowed and her whistle screamed.

I took a deep breath and nodded. I couldn't leave him with the wolf, so we two odd ducks waddled back down the hall toward Room 403.

Inside the classroom, a tower of reading journals waited for my response. Brian read from the elements book, quizzing me on chemical symbols as I tried to write a letter to a child who complained the *Indian in the Cupboard* book didn't tell the movie right.

On another day, Brian's screams caused Mrs. Westcott to poke her head into my classroom. She pointed her finger at him, and her eyes bored a hole through my forehead. "I would never stand for that!" She stabbed the air with her finger, cat-claw exposed.

She implied Brian was naughty and strict discipline could control his behavior, a bit like putting a bee in a jar and shaking it until the poor thing fell to the bottom.

I was overwhelmed, too, and managed my meltdowns by giving students art supplies to keep them engaged in meaningful tasks. They built fraction and percent models and created electrical circuits out of paper chains. Accumulating debris on the floor revealed my overload. I couldn't organize instructional materials and started to hide messes behind closed cabinet doors.

Sometimes, I let lessons slide, turned off the lights, and sat by the window to read aloud. My brain rested with closed inner eyes, listening to the story.

At home, I wanted the lights and television off and the telephone shoved down the garbage disposal. Boundless and irrational irritability abraded my twenty-five-year marriage.

One night, Joel leaned over the recliner and rubbed my shoulders. "How was your day?"

"It fucking sucked."

Joel, a gentle man who would do anything to help, withdrew into the kitchen to start dinner.

A callus formed that protected our relationship from bumps and bruises, but at a cost. We withdrew into separate experiences of shared days. The mistake of learning to live with my malignant thought processes stopped us from dealing with their source. Leaving well enough alone was killing us.

I ruminated on my days as if doing so might reveal hidden messages. Administrators evaluated, colleagues expected, parents demanded, and students needed. No amount of preparation helped me negotiate the entangled web that sapped my strength.

Brian and I grew more fatigued trying to meet the expectations set forth by the school. We formed a feedback loop, each irritated by the other. Our misery rubbed off; Room 403 filled with prickly people.

In January, I called the IEP team together again. "I want to send him to the behavior room before he escalates. I know the signs."

"You want to send him out while he is still okay?"

"No. I want to help him gain control before he can't." The team agreed he needed an option. The behavior teacher acquiesced by allowing him to spend time in her classroom.

With this plan, the sticky-wicket was that Brian had free rein in the hall between Room 403 and Mrs. Taylor's classroom. His temper tantrums became well designed retaliatory harpoons thrown at me because I made him leave the room.

One morning, I prepared Brian for a handwriting lesson. "Bri, we're going to practice *r.* Do you want to try one with me first?"

He slid down in his chair until he almost dropped from his seat, his long legs extended so far his knees hit the far edge of his desk. "Oh, no. Not *r.* I hate *r.*"

"Sorry, we're practicing *r* today. You're uncomfortable, so take your writing folder or book to Mrs. Taylor's room. At nine-thirty, it'll be time to come back. It's okay if you forget; I'll call you before we start silent reading."

Brian slammed his pencil on his desk, breaking the lead. "See what you made me do? Now I can't do *r!*" He rose from his chair and thrashed his way to the door. Then, he inched his way forward with baby steps. On the third floor tile, he turned around and screamed at me, "I hate you. You picked *r* on purpose. You didn't give me a chance. I was just gonna get paper. I was getting ready to do *r.*"

The rest of the children kept their eyes on their work, avoiding the commotion. Brian's temper tantrum garnered the attention he sought. Mrs. Westcott stepped around him to peek her head in my door. "Brian is screaming in the hall."

No shit.

⁂

In March, Mrs. Westcott called an IEP meeting. I appreciated her support, not anticipating I would be the problem. I thought my efforts deserved an A+. Mrs. Westcott disagreed. She made a solid case to the IEP team; I was inept.

- I was unable to control my students (Brian).
- I was disorganized.
- I exercised poor judgment.
- My students didn't raise their hands or walk in straight lines.

I hunched over in my chair. My voice cracked. "Brian takes a lot of my time."

The principal offered to observe me. The behavior teacher wanted to show me how to organize folders. The guidance counselor suggested she and I have tea once a week. "Just to check in, okay?"

The team nodded. *Tsk, tsk, tsk, such a shame.*

The guidance counselor summed it up. "Brian is your student. He needs you to be on your toes."

"I'm the teacher of nineteen other students who also need me!"

"Yes, but you're Brian's teacher." The rest of the team nodded their agreement.

I stood up, tears streaming down my face, crossed the threshold, then slammed the door behind me.

The closed door didn't shield me from the guidance counselor's voice. "She's an emotional mess."

My clumsy attempt at explaining myself failed. Neither Brian nor I stood a chance. There was no safety net at Jefferson Elementary School.

What you see is only a tiny part of me. Like ice floating in a
primal sea, consciousness sits uneasily on top of the whole me.
—Arden Georgi Thompson

Unfurling

I was a bug, impaled on a long, black pin, helplessly wiggling while
I tried to be a real teacher to the other children in Room 403.
Some of us reacted to the stress physically. My stomach knotted, and
I needed to vomit at the most inopportune moments. One little girl
developed migraine headaches; another made frequent trips to the
nurse. Sloane took to pacing like a little professor trying to ferret
out the solution to a mystery. Room 403 had lost its magic, and its
inhabitants grew irritable.

Each day, on the way to school and again on the way home, I
passed a walk-in clinic. Within the first minutes of April vacation,
my car followed the last bus out of the school's parking lot. I
made a spur-of-the-moment decision and abruptly turned into the
clinic's driveway.

Inside, the receptionist smiled and asked how she could help.

"I just need to get through June." I showed her my insurance card
and then sat down and thumbed through old magazines until it was
my turn.

A nurse practitioner entered the examining room and pulled my
chart up on her computer. "What brings you in?"

"I have a student who screams every day, and I am beginning to
feel like I might scream back."

"Every day?"

I interpreted her raised brow as doubt of the veracity of my statement. "*Every* day."

"Are you sleeping?"

"Not very well." I didn't elaborate. Most nights, I paced from bed to chair to refrigerator to bathroom back to bed from dusk until a few hours before the arrival of dawn's first light.

The nurse practitioner asked about menopause.

"I've only had a couple of periods since school started." If there was more I should have shared with her, I was oblivious of the fact.

She asked about meds.

I hadn't taken antidepressants for several years and jokingly bragged about being drug-free, clean of amitriptyline.

She looked me in the eye. "Let's get you back on it. I'll give you thirty days of Ativan too. You need to see your primary care physician, okay?"

⁂

I set the amber vial of Ativan on the windowsill above the kitchen sink. Forty-five days remained until the end of the school year, and there were only thirty white tablets of promised relief. I needed to use them judiciously. Since I was on vacation for the week, I didn't take any right away, saving them for those days when Brian's outbursts sent an electric shock to my jaw.

Spring break evoked a memory of clean white sheets snapping in the cold wind. A burst of energy celebrated the season's increased hours of sunlight. I looked forward to emptying a room of its contents, laying walls, windows, and floors bare for a thorough scrub.

Saturday morning, Joel picked his way to the coffee pot through piles of books, lamps, my fossil collection, and other contents that usually resided in the living room. He studied me. "I thought you were tired."

"I'm exhausted, but I couldn't sleep, so I started spring cleaning. Can you get muffins for us? The cinnamon kind, okay?" I pushed his travel mug, already filled with hot coffee, across to him and fluttered my eyelashes.

Joel laughed. "Anything for you, little girl." He kissed the top of my head. "Think you can clear the table by the time I get back?" He grabbed his jacket and headed out.

I ignored the pile of clutter on the table and pushed and shoved the living room furniture into the kitchen to surprise him. The entertainment center bested me; one of its components stuck, trapping me with it.

When Joel returned, white bakery bag in hand, he found me bracing the TV between the cabinet's lower shelf and my knee. I couldn't maneuver it to the floor as I had neglected to unplug it, and its weight prevented me from moving it back.

Joel closed the front door. "Need help?"

"Nope."

He leaned against the wall and peeled the paper wrapping from his muffin. His eyes teased. "Looks like you need help."

"Just unplug the damned thing!"

He did, then carried the heavy TV to the kitchen as if it weighed no more than a moth's wing.

I filled a bucket with hot soapy water and added ammonia, lifting the bottle as though pouring fine wine.

"Aren't you going to eat your muffin?"

"Later. I'm going to wash the ceiling. Can you get the ladder?"

I had never washed the ceilings in the past, and the glaring omission made me frantic to set it right.

Joel delivered the ladder, then fled into the backyard where April ice hid under winter-rotted mounds of moldering leaves. The rake scraped as he worked his way across our lawn.

After I wetted every square inch of the ceiling, water began to condense on the chilled windows. I opened the front door for ventilation, then tipped the cloudy water down the drain and refilled my bucket.

I washed the windows, then the floors. I pictured myself as a penitent nun on her knees, scouring the worn stones of a cathedral's nave. I dragged my rag across the carpet in huge sweeping arcs matching the rhythmic sound of Joel's rake. The task pulled tension from my muscles.

Grimy from head to toe, I grabbed my muffin and joined Joel in the backyard, where he loaded dead grass into the pickup. His efforts with the lawn looked better than my carpet. He'd left a pattern of perfect triangles behind him as he raked. It looked as if he had vacuumed the grass.

Logic skipped a beat. I demanded we buy a new vacuum; getting one was as essential to my well-being as breathing. Joel must have recognized no power in the universe would convince me otherwise.

After leaving the dump, we stopped at a local furniture store that sold small appliances. Within seconds, I chose the expensive garnet-hued vacuum. Joel compared the specifications of every model on the showroom's floor to mine. He should have known color trumped cost or airflow.

Once home, Joel carried the big box into the living room, then sat at the kitchen table to read the owner's manual.

I pulled the vacuum from the box and plugged it in.

"Beth, can't you wait two seconds for anything? The rug isn't dry!"

I conceded the point and turned it off in a huff.

His patience worn thin, Joel escaped back outside under the pretext of washing the truck.

I picked up the warranty papers, tossed the box down the basement stairs, then started lunch. The garnet jewel waited in the living room and proved too enticing to resist.

I left the sandwiches on the counter.

When I finished, the damp carpet looked glorious, its pile arranged in triangles as perfect as Joel's. The glory of it made my thoughts dance.

"Good waiting, babe."

Joel's sarcasm was lost on me. I grinned. "Thanks!"

"I'd have rented a carpet cleaner, you know." He added a handful of potato chips to his plate. "How's the vacuum?"

"I love it!" A clot of thoughts about cleaning surfaces vied for my attention. The ceiling, walls, and floor sparkled. The outside of the house needed to match. "We need a pressure washer to do the siding." I had thoughts of scrubbing the shingles on the roof.

"Good one!" Joel set his plate on a pile of books that still cluttered the table. "I've got to get to the lumber yard before it closes and go see Mom. Want to move the furniture back before I go?"

"Yes!" I brushed crumbs from the table onto the floor, taking note of where they fell so I could vacuum them later.

Joel and I lifted the pieces of furniture back to their usual spots. A bit of sand in the groove where the front door's threshold met the carpet marred the entire room, so I gave the area a quick swipe, then set the vacuum cleaner on the porch, out of the way.

I forgot to unplug it.

Joel left to run errands. The late afternoon temperature dipped, so I closed the windows. Before shutting the door, I noticed sand on the porch's weathered boards. Luckily, the vacuum cleaner was conveniently nearby. I checked to make sure he hadn't returned, then flicked the switch and vacuumed the porch. The sound of sand grains traveling through the hose delighted me.

Ant nests marred the clean lines of the sidewalk. The vacuum pulled me to the concrete as if I held the leash of an overeager dog. High notes echoed through the hose when an ants' nest disappeared, then changed to a low-pitched roar, which pushed me onto the next.

The cord stopped me short.

Joel stored extension cords in his workshop, so I headed downstairs to pilfer a long, thick orange one coiled around a reel. Then, I changed the bag and returned to my task.

Cars passed the house. I moved like an actress on stage from the sidewalk to the street gutter. Striated sand islands around the telephone pole broke into chunks and rattled as they slurred up the pneumatic tube until they filled the bag. I imagined a news team racing to the scene to ask for an interview.

And then, the vacuum cleaner quit. The silence stilled my breathing.

I turned, and there stood my husband, framed by the front door, holding the extension cord's plug in his hand. "What the hell are you doing? Beth, for Christ's sake, it's brand new. At least use the old one!"

Thank God! Relief flooded through me. The vacuum wasn't broken so there was no need to explain.

※

That evening, evicted dust motes moved across the street light. They seemed unsure about where to resettle, or perhaps they were celebrating their release. Joel watched TV, as usual, unaware I sat in darkness, thinking about death. Melancholy danced me to the edge of the abyss, and I revisited the sore spot that had plagued me since fourth grade.

Suicide's crackling voice spoke its mind. *Facts are facts; you are pathetic and an embarrassment to boot. What the hell were you thinking?* Worse, it told me the truth. *You can't keep this up, you know.*

My everyday thinking included suicidal ideations. Listening to my brain peruse my demise was as much a part of my routine as brushing my teeth or watching the news. In the same exaggerated way the vacuum cleaner led me onto the street, an amplified desire to end my life mired my mood.

I tossed and turned all night, then toward morning, I drifted off and dreamed about my first therapist. She handed me pillows. "Hit them. Get your anger out." I watched as red, green, and gold pillows burst like fragile Christmas ornaments. The sound was authentic—in the kitchen, Joel cracked eggs while making breakfast.

※

Thirty years ago, I had christened that particular therapist "Yoga Girl." She was young, earnest, and lithe. She believed pounding pillows and executing a perfect salute to the sun would clean away the spider's web that suffocated my heart and mind.

After three months of weekly sessions, enough was enough. I had emoted until as red-faced as a constipated child, but nothing moved. I gathered my belongings and planned never to darken her door again.

"Oh!" she exclaimed. "Wait! I found an article the other day. It seemed just right for you." She rifled through her file cabinet. "Here, I made a copy. The author suggests shattering glass."

I raised an eyebrow; the idea intrigued me.

"In a metal trash can, of course."

"That sounds exciting."

She bobbed her head. "Very cathartic." Her sincerity was endearing.

On the last Saturday of spring break, I snuck away from Joel, intent upon giving Yoga Girl's strategy a final chance. It never occurred to me a missing car and wife might be conspicuous clues to him that something was afoot.

Signs stapled to telephone poles advertised yard sales. I cruised through town and bought anything that would shatter. Inspired, I went to Walmart to purchase sets of glassware. In a flash of brilliance, I headed for the home decor aisle, looking for mirrors. Why not tempt fate?

Joel waited on the porch as I pulled into the driveway. He leaned across the railing. "Where'd you go?" His head lowered to inspect the back seat, piled high with boxes and bags. "Need help?"

"Nope." I was grateful he couldn't see into the trunk. "Just going to put a few things in the basement."

He went inside and turned on the TV.

I opened the daylight basement door and piled my goods near his table saw.

Joel stored the sledgehammer in the darkest corner of our old stone basement. We had bought it when he and I built our first house.

The hammer, a keepsake, had moved four times with us. I carried it past the table saw and workbench. Its polished wooden handle felt familiar in my hands.

Joel had an impeccable ability to sense when I trespassed into his workshop. He opened the door to the basement stairs. "What are you doing?"

"Just getting the sledgehammer."

"Why the hell do you want that?" He stepped onto the first stair tread.

I carried the sledgehammer toward the laundry area.

The second step creaked under Joel's weight. He turned on his heel. "Never mind, I don't want to know."

The floor creaked as he walked to the kitchen. The sound of water moving through the pipes and the clink of stoneware told me he'd started the dishes.

I emptied boxes and removed protective packaging with the abandonment of tearing through presents on Christmas morning. I arranged the glass into a symmetrical peacock's tail. Hot flashes roiled under my skin, sweat beaded across my forehead and back.

Yoga Girl's ghost cautioned me from the sideline. "You forgot the trash can! Get a trash can!"

I stood up to her by ignoring the voice in my head that advocated for my safety. I planned to emote as never before and allow the percussion to pulverize my angst. The moment of promised healing neared.

I knelt and slammed the hammer through a tower of plates without breaking the bottom two.

The sound of Joel's footsteps exploded on the floor above me.

I slipped outside my body and watched myself slam the hammer down again.

Yoga Girl criticized. *Jesus Christ, you can't even break glass right!* Then, her ghost screeched with delight. *Try again! You can do it!*

More glass shattered as Joel burst through the door and started down the stairs. "Beth, what the hell are you doing?" He stopped and stared.

"Just breaking some glass!" my voice squealed, my vocal cords as tense as the rest of my body. My face reddened as ripples of menopausal heat baked my skeleton.

Joel turned and left me alone to finish my task. I had no idea what he thought; I was too enthralled by the explosive movements and splintering sounds to care. After I finished, a hundred thousand shards of glass lay scattered on the concrete floor.

My skin flushed in hot pulsing patterns resembling those of a cuttlefish signaling its mate.

Joel returned to the basement. He paused to take in the scene, then extended his hands to pull me to my feet. He removed a sliver of glass from my cheek, then held me in his arms. "Little girl, little girl. What's going on?"

I leaned into his strength, needing his calmness, holding on for dear life. "Joel, I don't know. I'm scared."

"What is there to be scared of?" He pulled me closer.

I sobbed. "I'm scared of being alive. I can't remember things. I can't keep up. I can't think. I hate school. Nothing works, and I don't want to keep trying."

"No more, Beth. This is crazy. Flush those pills down the toilet and call the doctor."

I hadn't touched the Ativan because I was saving it for when I returned to school, and the amitriptyline was nothing new to my system. But calling Dr. Grant, my primary care physician, would appease Joel.

～

During my appointment, Dr. Grant asked the standard questions about menopause. "When did you have your last period?"

"A few months ago."

"How's it going?" Her unbuttoned white lab coat covered a lavender dress that didn't match her orange shoes.

"Things are getting hectic." Then, I told her about Brian, not sleeping for days, and vacuuming the road.

"You didn't!" Dr. Grant laughed, and so did I.

I didn't think to mention the glass shard fountain.

"What about your depression?"

"I have a pretty good exit plan." My words screamed suicidal despair, but I was the only one who heard the urgency because I delivered the line with feigned humor.

"Well, let's give the amitriptyline another chance." Dr. Grant opened the door. "Let me know if you have any problems."

On Monday morning, I returned to school with two white Ativan tablets hidden in my pocket. There was nothing to do but greet Room 403 and listen to vacation adventures from twenty little people who thought I was capable of listening.

What whole truth is no one of us can ever really say,
only that tiny, colored part we experience each day. And not
until we've collected all these bits and joined them with insight's
glue can we even begin to hazard a guess as to what Humpty
Dumpty truth looked like when it was whole and new.
—Arden Georgi Thompson

Goodbye, June

On the last day of school, my furtive attempt to restore order to Room 403 began at five-thirty in the morning. My car rolled into the parking lot with the lights off, and I parked in the janitor's spot. I took no chances of alerting others to my presence since I intended to move contraband.

Inside the dark school building, the familiar became strange. The rising sun cast peculiar shadows into the hall, making it easy to imagine monsters lurked in corners. The sound of my footsteps echoed off the cinderblock.

Mrs. Westcott's floor tiles gleamed, and her well-organized materials on open shelving prattled on about her capability. Colorful end-of-school gift bags awaited each child. On her desk, perfect piles of writing folders and reading journals were ready to go home with students.

Room 403 resembled a disaster of biblical proportion. I needed Moses to part the mess. Rather than organize the jumbled entanglement, my plan was to shuttle everything into my car, trash and all, to be sorted at home. My brain hammered two messages. Hurry! Hide! What if I got caught throwing away school supplies? Only I knew I planned on buying replacements.

My trunk filled with announcements I'd forgotten to send home, photocopies of worksheets I'd meant to use, math workbooks, and the reading journals I'd abandoned during the *Indian in the Cupboard* days. Each armload of rubbish lugged out of the building tightened the knot of anxiety in my gut.

Disorganized manipulatives, dirty science equipment, and discarded student projects worked their way into the gaps between wasted paper. Craft supplies spilled into every remaining nook and cranny. A new planbook and my teacher's manuals landed on the floorboards; my personal belongings piled on top.

Outside, a green metal dumpster situated against the school's back wall offered to eat the mess so Joel wouldn't know about my problem. Stupid! If I were to use it, the janitor would find it filled to overflowing and run to Mr. Blanchard to announce I had invented a previously unknown way to be wrong.

Returning inside, I unlocked the janitor's closet, reached in, and snitched his broom. By seven o'clock, my area bore a resemblance to Mrs. Westcott's pristine classroom in a Goodwill, scruffy sort of way. Minus the gifts, of course.

A bead of sweat ran down my temple, and my shirt stuck to my back. Against all common sense, I unplugged my fan and scurried to toss it into the back seat of my convertible.

The janitor greeted me as I re-entered the building. "Borrowed a broom, did you?"

I hung my head. "Yes."

"I'd have helped, you know."

I knew he would have, but, more than anyone else, the compassionate man knew about my confusion because he swept around it every afternoon. I didn't want to see my world through his eyes; I needed privacy.

He spun his keyring around his finger. "I had to park by the dumpster. Tell me when you move your car."

At that moment, it dawned on me that the wetness between my thighs wasn't sweat. I had missed my period for months, and physiology chose this day to begin the last time I would bleed.

After dealing with the predicament, I washed up as well as I could with paper towels. A glimpse of myself in the mirror revealed something stuck to my skirt. I brushed at it, but to my horror, I realized it was a bloodstain. My face flushed with embarrassment thinking the janitor may have seen.

Oversized sweatshirts from the lost and found were the only disguise available—one to wrap around my waist and the other to pull over my sweat-soaked shirt. Then, I moved my car and returned to the safety of Room 403, a ransacked space swept clean. I straightened the desks, sorted books, and took the bulletin board down.

The janitor brought a hot bucket of soapy water.

My gaze focused on his left temple, the closest I could get to eye contact. "Thank you." I washed shelves and cleaned the desktops, removing tell-tale traces of markers, pencil lead, glue, and grime.

Mrs. Westcott poked her head through the doorway. "How's it going?" Her eyes scanned the room. "Do you have enough shaving cream?"

"What?"

"You didn't know?" She flipped her ponytail. "Fourth-graders clean their desks with shaving cream; it's a tradition."

I stared at her through slitted eyes. It was one thing to hurt me, but to rob my fourth-graders of the memory was despicable.

Before she turned to leave, she arched her catty eyebrows to call attention to my sweatshirts. "Really? It's going to be hot today."

It slipped out. "No shit."

The bell rang; students entered the building helter-skelter, abandoning straight lines: the emergence of the herd I loved. I never liked the elementary school's formality, although I developed a respect for how hand-raising and straight-line-walking helped cogs turn. Overnight, my fourth-graders had shed their skins, revealing themselves as fifth-graders. They had already severed their ties with the elementary school and were ready to move on to a new building, albeit with varying degrees of anxiety.

Brian missed the last morning which meant one less bit of chaos. That thought gave rise to guilt. Had I done something to keep him away?

Instead of reading stories from students' writing folders, as the other fourth-grade teachers did, I took Room 403 outside onto the forbidden grass of the athletic field. I passed my car and retrieved a large glass cookie jar filled with 1,747 marbles (Brian had counted them before Christmas break) from its back seat.

The marbles fell from my hands onto the grass as if to feed chickens. "No hands. The person who gets the most marbles into the jar wins the honor of being the person who gets the most marbles into the jar."

They stopped to figure out what I meant. Then, as on the first day of school, they waited for my prompt, pausing again, probably for the last time in their school career.

"It's okay to take your shoes off." I flicked my sandals to the grass and picked up a marble with my toes. Soon, all of my chicks followed suit.

Off to the side, sweltering in extra layers, I basked in the presence of children united in laughter. "Come on, Mrs. Davis!" I ignored the sweatshirts and played, as much a newborn fifth-grader as they.

The last morning with my students wound down to its inevitable conclusion. Room 403 exploded again as desks emptied, backpacks filled, fights erupted, and excited children anticipated summer vacation.

The intercom interrupted. "Teachers, remember your report cards and the notes that need to go home."

Jolly good. Despite many years of experience, my raggedy nerves and tattered memory would have forgotten that part.

Once my room emptied, I listened to the banter of other teachers who whooped and hollered in anticipation of summer vacation. I wished to chime in, too, but I closed the door, knowing I was an outlier. I told myself I had pencils that needed sharpening.

Brian's mom peeked in. "We stopped by to get Bri's report card. You don't mind if we come in, do you?"

I did mind. "Of course not. I'm glad you're here!" What else do you say when you see a friend with donuts and coffee in hand?

Mrs. Westcott popped in. Brian abandoned emptying his desk and ran to her, forgetting to respect her personal space. "I passed; I'm a fifth-grader too!"

She stepped back. "Well, have a good summer." Then, she turned on her heel and left.

I high-fived the kid who vanquished the witch.

Brian's mother closed his backpack. "Time to go, Bri. We haven't got all day. Do you have everything?"

He dragged his backpack across the room and disappeared into the hall. His mother and I hugged before she followed.

The sound of Brian throwing his backpack so high it hit the ceiling made me think of the first time I had met him. Thunk, swish, thunk. The knot in my throat burned. Silence beat against my eardrums.

"I'll miss you, Mrs. Davis." The voice belonged to Brian, who had returned to hide behind the door.

I went into the hall and held that child's face in my hands; we looked into each other's eyes. "You did good, you know."

Brian nodded. He buried his dark hair into my shoulder. I hadn't noticed how tall he'd grown. "Goodbye, Brian."

Then, he disappeared again. In true Asperger fashion, he ran back to quiz me on the elements. His mom came to fetch him and steered him away, rolling her eyes at me.

I laughed and shook my head, thinking of the day Brian had played the part of a snail in the hall. I wrapped the framed Periodic Table of Elements poster in discarded bulletin board paper and leaned it against my desk.

The intercom intruded again. "Teachers, please check your mailboxes before you go to lunch."

In mine, a note from the principal sent a shiver down my spine. *Beth—Have a good summer. Rest and recuperate. We should talk sometime. Mr. B.* I felt certain the words weren't a friendly overture.

A second envelope contained a behavior rating scale to complete on Brian's behalf for a pediatric psychologist named Dr. Holland.

I knew better than to take the long survey back to Room 403 because something ate paper in there. I sat at the table in the office, borrowed a pen, and began.

Psychologists used rating scales to evaluate students. This one required me to compare Brian's behavior with that of his peers.

Items on the rating scale included:

- Does not follow through on instructions or fails to finish tasks. *(He didn't, and come to think of it, neither did I.)*
- Remembers daily activities *(Nope, but then how could he when I didn't?)*
- Organizes tasks and activities *(No, but then, again, was it his fault or mine?)*
- Keeps track of things necessary for activities *(Well, Brian was better at this than me.)*

Lightning flashed through my brain as I connected the dots. My agitation, sleeplessness, and irritability might be undiagnosed attention deficit disorder. What if all the therapists I had worked with over the years were ineffective because they looked under the wrong stone? What if medication might help?

The intercom squealed. "Teachers, there will be a brief meeting in the library at one o'clock. Attendance is mandatory."

I slid Brian's evaluation into Dr. Holland's envelope, dropped it into the mail bin, and headed for the library.

The principal revealed the district's plan to start a program designed to meet the needs of students with autism during the next school year. We were to work in teams to brainstorm ideas for the program.

At the table, I faced Mrs. Westcott. Her ponytail bounced as she expounded upon her interpretation of best practices. I wished I had saved two Ativan. I was barely able to forgo explaining to her that stringent discipline wasn't the magic solution.

The battle belonged to a new generation of teachers. Tired, I withdrew from the conversation, trusting the district would hire someone wiser than Mrs. Westcott to implement a quality program for autistic students.

The principal closed his notebook and left us to our business. Forty-five minutes later, the intercom stopped the conversation. "Teachers, you may leave the building when you have completed the end-of-the-year checklist. You'll need each item signed off by the custodian or me. Thank you."

And so the end began.

I left my peers to drink their coffee and chat. I had isolated myself from the faculty rather than make new acquaintances. The shield I had constructed hurt, and I walked to my room, grieving the consequence of avoidance: loneliness.

I picked up my cumulative folders, official "scrapbooks" filled with copies of report cards, test results, and other vital documents. Each year, the guidance counselors migrated the folders from one teacher's slot to the next in a large filing cabinet. For more than a hundred years, this archaic practice had been a rite of passage.

I had filled out hundreds of folders during my career, but this year brain fatigue set in quickly. Setting aside my pen, I penciled in detailed information. After double-checking and erasing errors, I traced the pencil marks with ink. My signature officially promoted a child to fifth grade.

I lagged far behind my usual pace.

The guidance counselor hovered outside my door like a lone buzzard. One by one, I completed the damned folders, cursing each one for life. I handed the tall pile to her with feigned politeness and cast an evil spell on her as she walked away. *Drop them, drop them.*

I had earned the right to turn my lights off and close my door. Even the guidance counselor agreed. I was finished.

*Perhaps today would never have been, and tomorrow could
never be without what happens to each of us when we wander
off to pick flowers and find ourselves along the way.*
—Arden Georgi Thompson

Between Cause and Consequence

At home, summer began when four black trash bags disappeared into the maw of a garbage truck. No flies buzzed around the evidence of my deterioration; at least I'd kept half–eaten lunches from the mix.

Charging replacement parts to my credit card solved the problem of damaging the school's materials. I ordered a second set for my personal use, which seemed prudent because I'd no longer need to justify how I took care of them. The onus was on me.

I pretended all was well and contemplated wrapping myself in a shroud.

⁂

During the first week of summer vacation, I made an appointment with Dr. Grant to get a second opinion about my self-diagnosis of attention deficit disorder. I was sure that if I shared the behavior rating scale with her, she'd see the same pattern and give me a different type of white pill that would mend my frayed edges.

"I think maybe I've had it all along, and no one knew. Is that possible?"

Dr. Grant fiddled with the pens buried in her white lab coat's pocket. "Could be."

"It wouldn't hurt to try something, would it?"

"I don't see why not."

She wrote a script for Strattera, which added a stimulant to my hormonal stew and the amitriptyline. "Let me know if you have any problems."

Morning sunshine woke me on the second Sunday of vacation. The familiar sound of Joel working in the kitchen wrapped me in an intangible hug. I padded downstairs to join him, stepping around our raggedy cat, who slept in sunlight that streamed through the window.

"Morning, babe." He kissed my forehead. "Any plans for today?"

I hugged him, took the hot mug of coffee he offered and sat in the living room to watch the news. "The garden looks awful. I think I'll weed and go to the nursery."

Joel settled in the recliner. "I'm going to invite Mom and Kim over around eleven."

"Of course you are; why have a good day?" My snarky comment captured my attitude. I knew his mother's and sister's conversation would devolve into the same argument about who did what, when, where, and why as it had the last umpteen times we'd entertained them.

For me, hell was the patio table.

Joel didn't react to my rudeness.

I weeded the garden while I waited for his family's intrusion.

Joel came out of the basement's garden door to empty my wheelbarrow, then ducked back into his workshop.

I followed him inside.

"What are you doing?"

I laughed at his undertone of worry that I might be on the verge of smashing more glass. "Just getting the shovel."

Joel grabbed it and escorted me out of the basement. "Show me where you want to dig."

The black soil didn't resist. Joel dug two deep holes and was working on the third when his mom and sister arrived. He set the shovel against the fence. "Whoa, Mom and Kim are here. We'll finish up later."

The day seemed no different than any other Sunday. However, a magnificent bolt of irritation crackled through my brain, and I abandoned civility. Blood rushed to my temples.

I walked toward them, fighting the desire to flip the table and shoo our visitors back to their cars as if they were stray dogs who had pooped on the grass. The stone wall that separated the slope of the garden from the yard interrupted my journey. I stopped to pluck at strawberry runners that cascaded over the garden's stone wall.

Joel's shadow passed by as he carried the veggie tray and wine from the refrigerator to the patio. "Aren't you going to join us?"

I didn't answer. My brain screamed *Hell no!* Then it made the connection to a Vietnam protest slogan familiar to any child of the sixties. *Hell no, I won't go.* Each time my imagination chanted the words, my rage intensified.

Minutes passed. I turned to glare at what I believed to be a captive and shocked audience, but no one responded to my nonverbal message. Didn't they get it? Combing through the dirt was better than sitting at their goddamned table.

Joel's mother took the bait. "Beth, what are you doing?"

The answer was obvious; I was sitting on the grass, as any dumb fuck could see.

The what-are-you-doing question was tricky. When Joel asked me what I was doing, the words were a warning to stay away from his things. Sometimes, my friends called and used the question as a prelude to an invitation. My father used the phrase as an accusation. At work, my colleagues teased. My students were the only honest ones; they wanted to know what I was doing.

I wasn't about to guess which version Joel's mother tossed my way.

Joel and his family ignored me. Instead of being cordial, I returned to my quiet house and curled up in the recliner. From outside the window, their laughter and predictable arguments about events long past cut like Brian's screams. Loneliness engulfed me. I felt shunned and companionless, even though I could hear familiar voices.

I was an outlier again, with no idea I was the one who had turned my back on them. It didn't matter if they were inches away or a hundred feet. I didn't fit. While this feeling was nothing new, the magnitude of my distress skyrocketed.

I raged silently.

Recognizing my rudeness, I rose from my chair and opened the front door. I meant to go to the patio to apologize. Time slowed and objects receded into blackness. I descended the first porch step, the second, and then the third. When my foot hit the cement sidewalk, I stepped between cause and consequence.

The cement walkway disappeared as if it were a chalk drawing in the rain. My home may as well have belonged to a stranger. I watched Joel's animated body while he chatted with his family as I uncoupled from my marriage.

There was no gradient; the event was a conversion, not a decision. I had a husband; then, without having had a fight, he was gone. It was as if our entanglement dissolved, leaving only flesh; he died right in front of me without flatlining.

No one else noticed the ripple that shuddered from one edge of the universe to the other.

Joel disappeared. He was, then he wasn't.

I overheard goodbyes and a car door closing. Joel entered the house through the side door carrying empty wine glasses and the decimated veggie platter.

I didn't think to protect him or explain. "I decided to get an apartment." The announcement caught me by as much surprise as it did him.

"What are you talking about?"

"I don't want to do this anymore."

Joel stopped and looked at me. "You know what?" A considerable pause followed; he shifted the wine glasses in his grip. "I don't either."

I don't know how he reached his conclusion; was there more to it than me changing my job without notice, a new vacuum cleaner, or splintered glass?

My heart recognized danger, skipped a beat, and then continued on its journey. If my brain were scooped from my skull, it might have glowed in the dark.

The next day, the morning sun lit the bedroom the same way it had the day before. The birds hid, and the holes in the garden no longer held dreams; they were cavities.

Joel made coffee, and the aroma worked its way upstairs. When I came down, he didn't pour any into my mug.

"Good morning."

"Mornin'."

My mug rested inside its coffin. I opened the cabinet door, then closed it. Exhuming my cup would be an affirmation of my marriage's death. I felt numb and recognized I'd lost the self-assurance I had felt yesterday but kept up a false bravado. It didn't take long for euphoria to reignite.

At nine o'clock, Joel went to the bank to open a separate account. When he returned, I showed him an advertisement on Craigslist—a two-bedroom apartment in an old farmhouse, available for immediate occupancy. It was close to school, owner occupied, and affordable, heat and hot water included.

Joel read the ad. "Call them. If it's available, we'll look." He shook his head. "I need to know you're safe."

His comment reassured me. I signed the lease that afternoon.

And so, we stepped forward, husband and wife, moving in different directions. Later that evening, we sat at the kitchen table and talked about my instability for the first time in our twenty-three-year marriage.

Joel looked tired. "I tried to help."

"And you did, every minute of every day." I reached for his hand. "I couldn't figure out how to change into a different person." We talked about our shared memories and affirmed our love would last forever.

Practical matters kept us busy. Lying in the dark without touching the warmth of my husband's body hurt my soul. How could two people who were so close wind up so far apart?

Agreeing to the mechanics of our separation was easy; neither of us harbored animosity. We'd sell the house. Joel didn't want my fossil collection, and I didn't want anything in his workshop. There'd be no lawyers, no legal papers, no divorce decree.

We stayed married, packed up, and moved on.

Each day, I deposited boxes into my car and bused them up the hill to my new home. My son Sean, who was Joel's stepson, helped load my furniture into Joel's truck and took it to the farm where my second-floor apartment looked out over the valley. I could see the house I'd abandoned from the kitchen window.

Goats hurried to the fence when we arrived. They already knew to expect treats because I had been feeding them Cheetos each time I delivered boxes. Joel and Sean hauled my old trunk, a rocking chair, table, bookcase, and bed up the steep staircase.

Joel drove away in his empty truck, leaving Sean to shuttle the last of my books and rock collection into the new living room. "Are you sure you're going to be okay, Mom?"

"I'm fine." A wee lie—I felt as though I could harvest stars from the night sky.

"If you need anything, you call me." He opened my kitchen cabinets before he left. "What are you going to eat tonight?"

"I have peanut butter and syrup; I don't need anything else."

After Sean left, I laid on the floor, spread my arms wide, and experienced that delicious feeling of autonomy supported by uncertain capability for the first time in my life. I was single without knowing how to be alone. The wooden walls protected me from expectations I couldn't meet, from situations I misinterpreted, and from criticism I deserved.

An antique pan chandelier with three etched glass shades illuminated my new bedroom. Roses sat on a cardboard box near my bed-—the card read *Welcome Home, Love, Joel.* That was when I knew what I had lost. Confused tears blended with sad ones; rage vied with bliss. My brain had unleashed every emotion simultaneously and the torrent evoked evil.

A few days later, Joel called. I had never heard him cry before. "I need you," he said, his voice choking like it does when sobs are real.

I drove down the hill in the twilight to Joel's new apartment. We held each other and talked about the unexpected changes unfolding. Neither of us wanted to go backward, but our trajectory was taking us too far apart, too fast. I tried to reassure myself more than him. "We're breaking what needs to be broken; we'll figure it out."

"Girl, I don't want you to go."

I thought he was worried about me driving home in the dark; I missed his invitation to stay. "I'll be fine."

After the move, one of my first tasks was to buy groceries. I parked my car at a local supermarket. The automatic doors swooshed open. I grabbed a cart and pretended to be an assertive shopper who knew what she wanted. I searched each aisle for something to eat, repeated the process a second time, then a third.

My solution to indecision was to purchase seven cinnamon muffins, seven cans of chicken soup, seven cans of ravioli, two flavors of ice cream, and a week's worth of Cheetos for the goats. It didn't take long to realize I needed to return to the store for a can opener, toilet paper, soap, and other sundries that come in handy.

During the second attempt, I carried a new can opener around the store in my hand so I wouldn't forget it. Then, I set it on the shelf while I handled cans of vegetables, unable to decide if I should get the green ones or the yellow. That can opener never made it to the register either.

I ate cinnamon muffins for dinner and completed the task of buying a can opener the next day.

My brain didn't recognize it was in trouble—how could it? It had no external reference points to measure internal errors.

During the second week of August, our house went under contract. Only two weeks later, Joel and I met at the bank and passed our keys to my garden's new keepers' hands. The cavities waited for them to fill.

We settled into new routines after a marathon of shuttling our belongings. Joel's new apartment was only a few blocks away from the house we had sold. We missed each other. Now and then, we hung out and brushed the goats, talking about the changes we needed to make. Whenever Joel returned to his new apartment, I cried with the ululating cadence of a keening infant left alone for too long.

We named the huge tangled problem *It*.

Joel railed at the beast. "I need *It* to stop."

"I know. *It* will." I squeezed my eyes shut, willing it so. I meant it. I would lock *It* up and defy *It* to misbehave ever again.

*If I touch a rainbow, will the colors smear or soak unevenly into the
sky like paint onto coarse white paper when clouds heap gray and
sounds echo hollowly away? If not, I'll reach up and take pieces of
gold and green to nibble when night comes, or I feel sad and gray to
help me remember when "difficult" really wasn't and "impossible"
were the dares we made to each other to pass the summer's day.*
—Arden Georgi Thompson

The Turquoise Frigidaire

I glimpsed the circa-1950s turquoise-blue Frigidaire through my
daughter's car window as we drove by an antique store. It sat
against the back wall, only its rounded top visible. Its color, which
matched my classroom walls, arrested my attention as if my gaze
were a magnet passing over iron nails.

"Ali, stop!" I pointed to an open parking spot.

Allison hit the brakes. "Damn it, Mom, I can't park in front of a
fire hydrant."

While Allison searched for a legal parking space, I kept an eye on
the shop's door, ready to confront anyone who dared buy the refrigerator out from under me.

Inside, the whimsical shop displayed its wares against white
linens edged in lace; the air smelled of lavender and dusty wood. My
finger traced the handle of a white ironstone pitcher filled with dried
hydrangeas. "I'm going to get this too, Ali."

My daughter busied herself at a far shelf talking with the clerk.
I walked over to the old refrigerator. A *For Sale* sign hung from the
rusted door handle. "Allison, look, half price! God wants me to
buy it!"

"Do you see the part about no refunds or returns?" My practical daughter sounded less enchanted than I hoped.

I opened its heavy door and visualized stacks of colored construction paper displayed on its shelves, a rainbow of tempera paint in the door racks, and bouquets of paintbrushes arranged in the open-bottomed aluminum egg tray. Cuter than cute! The antique refrigerator would be my back-to-school birthday gift, a steal at $300.

"Mom, it won't fit in your room." Allison planted her fists on her hips, which struck me as funny—I was the parent, not her.

"Of course it will." Never mind that backpacks, snow pants, and boots flowed from the cramped coat closet into the classroom. Never mind that I couldn't fit a small round reading table into the corner near the windows. Never mind the tag's warning: *Final Sale, No Refund or Exchange.* Never mind I had promised to keep *It* under control.

Never mind, whispered the bipolar spider, luring me deeper into its web. The refrigerator matched the wall color. What else mattered?

I called Sean, who agreed to deliver it to my classroom. "Consider it an early birthday present, Mom."

The next morning, I asked the janitor to move his truck so we could unload the monstrosity onto the cement loading dock. His eyes rolled. "You aren't bringing that inside, are you?"

I bobbed my head, shivering with anticipation.

The janitor turned and walked toward the principal's office.

Sean jockeyed the refrigerator into my classroom. "Where do you want it?"

Room 403, of course, did not have a tile's worth of extra space. So, my son maneuvered it back outside into his truck. The janitor and Mr. Blanchard watched with icy stares from the far end of the hallway.

I called Allison. "It doesn't fit."

"Mom, I told you it wouldn't."

"I know, but what am I going to do now?" My eye twitched as if conversing with Allison's silence. "Can you keep it until I figure it out?"

"John's going to have a fit! Tell Sean to put it in the garage for now, but I can't keep it very long. You'll have to figure it out."

After an exhaustive search, the mother of a former student agreed to adopt it. She wanted to keep extra soda and beer in her barn. Sean moved it a third time.

꩜

On Sunday, Joel took me out for ice cream. Afterward, he needed to get back to his apartment, so before dusk quieted the goats, we made birthday plans for Wednesday.

The next day, Andrea from the Math and Science Coalition called. "Hey, Beth, would you do a workshop at Bigelow Lab for me?" She went on to explain how she had double-booked and needed a sub.

I loved presenting at workshops; they provided the perfect social environment for me. My leadership role separated me from the group without a hint of ostracism. Conversations centered around science content and student learning, not personal concerns. Strangers arrived without agendas, so I trusted their superficial banter would carry no hidden barbs. "Of course! When?"

"Wednesday."

That evening, when Joel called, I told him about the workshop.

"Wednesday, seriously?" He paused long enough that doubt passed through my mind.

"Yup! I can't wait."

Wednesday morning, after ransacking the apartment, I found my keys in the washer. Once in the car, I remembered I had spent the change I kept for tolls, but rather than return to my apartment to get more, I decided to avoid the fees by taking Route 1 instead of the turnpike.

As I drove north toward the lab, it dawned on me that it was my birthday. Joel and I had dinner plans. I stewed about not getting a card or a gift. Joel always left them by my morning coffee. What had happened? Never mind we no longer lived together. He'd promised, and he had a key.

I decided to show him. I'd buy my own damned gift! Never mind that I'd already purchased a refrigerator.

I passed through coastal towns, considering what to buy for myself. Sparkling giddiness steamrolled over common sense, and a little girl occupied my skin. She pranced down the garden path with a basket of flowers, tossing roses to the roaring crowd that didn't exist. I drove the car while she steered.

The little girl whispered, *Look for blue.* I pulled into the parking lot of the first shop with something blue in its front window. I forgot to shut off the engine. Once inside, I looked for the perfect gift. She tapped me on the shoulder and whispered again, *From me to you.*

The shopkeeper intercepted me after I had peeked and poked in every nook and cranny twice. "Are you looking for anything in particular?"

"That little Dorothy mouse, I think." I pointed to a locked case of figurines.

"Oh! One of the Wee Forest Folk! She's terribly cute, isn't she? I'll get the key."

I didn't think she was cute at all, but I could not renege; Toto and the Dorothy mouse wearing blue had chosen me, and it would have been rude to refuse. When the shopkeeper opened the case, I pointed to a second figurine. "I'll take that one, too. They're used to being next to each other. And the baby one. I don't want it to be scared."

The total came to over $200. A clash of orange- and red-colored tissue paper in the bag distracted me.

"Ma'am, don't forget your credit card."

I slipped it into my wallet and headed for the door a second time.

"Ma'am, don't forget your bag."

A disembodied male voice from about three feet away spoke into my left ear. "*The gift is in the giving.*"

The little girl steered me toward the next store. *Green, green!* Intent on *giving* gifts, I focused on the buildings near the road. *Leave the ugly mice by the door; they'll be a present for a stranger. We'll find something better!*

All the way up the coast, I bought colors, leaving the gift I chose near the next shop's door, and then purchased something new.

I bought a yellow platter from a shop with a yellow flag and then left it at the store with red geraniums, where I purchased red enamelware. I soon believed another person who shared my birth date followed me, as wrapped up in my scavenger hunt as I was.

I arrived at the lab a little late, but none of the teachers minded the extra downtime. I had presented countless times, so without preparation, I handed out materials. By two o'clock, we had finished our review of the state's newest version of the science learning standards. I repacked the books into their boxes, returned chairs to their tables, and threw loose papers into the trash.

The intensity of my adventure was exhilarating. When I arrived at my apartment, Joel opened the door and welcomed me with flowers and a kiss. On the table sat a cake, a card, and one of those perfect little jewelry boxes.

"I wanted to surprise you."

How could I have had so little faith in this man?

I wore my new pearl earrings to school the next day. In the early afternoon, Mr. Blanchard knocked on my door, then walked in. "How was your summer?"

"Good."

"Did you have a chance to rest?"

"I did!" I lied and stifled the polite question of asking about his summer.

"I think you should check your mailbox. There's something from Central Office."

Damn it. I followed him, paranoid enough to expect to be summarily fired. Instead, a white business-sized envelope forwarded from the middle school slid out of the interdepartmental mailer.

I ran my finger across the raised ridges of the scarlet insignia of Cornell University. The postmark indicated it had taken *four months* for the letter to follow me to my new position at Jefferson Elementary.

Dr. Cabrera's bold script decorated the envelope and the hand-written letter. My anxiety flew from a plummeting trapeze to one that swung upward while I read the short message:

Dear Beth,
    You are invited to the first Patterns of Thinking
Leadership Academy during the week of January 16th.
Please respond ASAP.
    Best regards,
    Derek

Mr. Blanchard hovered near the reception desk. I slid the note across the counter to him. "He's got to think I ignored his invitation."

He read it, then slid the note back. "You can use my office to call him if you'd like."

One of Derek's graduate students helped sort out the snarl. School would be in session in January, so I needed to apply for professional leave. I left the office with a sinking feeling. I had tarnished my sterling reputation by failing to cope with Brian and delivering a turquoise-blue Frigidaire to the building. There was no reason to expect Mr. Blanchard to present my case to the school board.

He had waited for me to emerge from his office. "How'd it go?"

"I haven't talked with Derek since I was at the middle school. I can't believe he even remembered me." I'd forgotten about my grandiose schemes and suddenly they were as real as the envelope in my hand.

"You must have done something very well. Come, have coffee and tell me more."

Over two of the worst cups of coffee I had ever tasted, I explained that Dr. Cabrera used the mathematical language of complexity theory to prove thinking emerges from four simple patterns. "Derek is the first person to take the act of thinking itself out of the black box. Other schools and businesses all over the world use his method. Why is it so hard to get people to explore this?"

"If you can find the head of the hydra, let me know."

I had surmised he was a staunch supporter of the status quo, but his wry smile hinted the education system frustrated him too.

"In seventh grade, I used thinking patterns to deconstruct science misconceptions. That's what interested Derek. I planned on sharing a few case studies with him, just anecdotal data. Do you think I could collect some again?"

"Are you helping students learn?"

I nodded.

"Then I don't see a problem. Go ahead, keep me informed. Don't use names, and stick to the curriculum."

"Thinking doesn't require different materials."

His approval and support surprised me. He still scared me, but that no longer mattered. I had an ally, and I would go to Cornell.

*Where is reality in the shifting, shimmering world I see when
I cannot draw lines of discrete existence around any living entity?*
—Arden Georgi Thompson

The Diamond Thumper

No matter how many times I experienced it, the first day of school was always the same. My inner child squirmed with tumultuous joy. Pristine gold and green boxes of crayons scented the air, and my new shoes made teacher-clicks when I walked down the hall. The prospect of meeting new students tantalized me. If a mayfly could be anything it wanted during the single day of its adult life, it would be me walking into my classroom: everything tidy and bursting with infinite potential.

Mrs. Westcott popped her head into my room. "Ready to go?" She scanned the premises. "Your room looks great, by the way. We were watching you pull it together."

Had she and the other teachers snickered behind my back when I realized the turquoise-blue Frigidaire wouldn't fit in my room? No, Mrs. Westcott referred to the obvious: my organized classroom appeared welcoming. Her invitation to walk to the playground caught me by surprise. With Brian gone, she seemed to have wiped the slate clean.

She flicked her ponytail. "I hope things are better this year."

"No shit!" The words popped out of my mouth before I could stop them.

Mrs. Westcott laughed.

Outside on the playground, I stood near the other teachers who covertly spied on the kindergarten mothers coping with separation anxiety.

Mrs. Westcott giggled at two grown women weeping on each other's shoulders. "We should set up a tissue station."

A second unexpected comment came from the prim and proper reading-recovery teacher. "I think we should serve drinks!"

I was unsure if she meant for us to sip while we watched or for the poor mothers to drink as pain relief. We split up with a chuckle, shucked our summer attitudes, and found our students so we could admire their new clothes, pencil boxes, and superhero notebooks.

The guidance counselor approached and pointed out a small girl hunkered down on the blacktop near the four-square court. "That's Lucy."

Her slight build made her appear more like a second-grader than a nine-year-old.

It had been a rough summer for Lucy. Her mother had found an improvised noose in her closet and called the school to make us aware of her struggle.

Like Brian, I had met the paper version of this child first. Lucy's inch-thick cumulative folder held evidence that math would panic her, and so would reading and writing. Changing grades was sure to provoke her anxiety because her learning disability widened the gap between her and her peers. I pictured Lucy balancing with one foot on the iceberg of her last year's teacher, the other on mine, with her classmates positioned like waiting killer whales anticipating a tasty morsel.

I crossed the playground and sat on the hot asphalt next to her. "Hello, Lucy. I'm your teacher. My name is Mrs. Davis." I didn't know what else to say. "You already know that, but I wanted to introduce myself, anyway."

Behind us, the swing set groaned and squealed as the stress from its weighted pendulums pulled at the tubular frame. A game of tag swept past us like a swarm of gnats. "I'm glad you're here."

"I'm not."

Her sagging shoulders and bowed head tugged at my heart. "Hmm. Is it okay for me to wait with you?"

Lucy shrugged her shoulders. I took the gesture to be an unstated invitation.

When the bell rang, we followed a confident pig-tailed tomboy to our classroom. Students found their desks and unloaded their backpacks. My third eye watched Lucy ditch her math workbook in the trash can.

That year, I cast my spell using two canning jars, each filled to the midpoint with a clear liquid. While I introduced myself, I walked between the aisles of desks, handing out sandwich-sized Ziploc bags filled with Styrofoam packing peanuts.

Returning to the front of the classroom, I stuffed a handful of Styrofoam peanuts into one of the jars while prattling on about unexpected events. A few dropped to the floor—it wasn't an exciting moment. "Dang." I looked at my audience with a deer-in-the-headlights expression. "They were supposed to fit."

A tall girl who carried herself like a ballerina rose from her seat. "Need help, Mrs. Davis?"

"I think so. Put the ones that fell in the other jar for me, will you?"

She dropped the strays into the second jar, and they vanished! Her eyes opened wide with confusion as if she had done something wrong.

The prairie dogs came out of their burrows, climbing over their desks to get a closer look. Those who missed the event jumped up, trying to identify the source of their classmates' wonderment. Lucy was the exception. Her forehead remained glued to the top of her desk.

I carried the magic jar around the room. Each time a student added a Styrofoam bead to the mysterious serum, it disappeared.

The intercom squawked. "Teachers, bus rehearsal will begin in five minutes."

The year was off to a promising start. I'd tucked a copy of my bus list inside my shoe so I wouldn't lose it. The original was in Mr. Blanchard's mailbox.

When Room 403 returned from our designated crack in the sidewalk, the mystery of the disappearing packing peanuts drew my students back. They took turns adding more to the jar, and again, each one dematerialized.

The intercom disrupted my classroom again. "Third lunch students should be in the cafeteria."

Damn it. I'd forgotten about lunch.

The office was visible from the cafeteria. A dozen long-stemmed yellow roses sat on the reception desk. I knew they were mine because Joel had given me long-stemmed roses on the first day of school every year since 1984.

I carried them back to my room. Mrs. Westcott passed me in the hall. "Gorgeous! Hey, you need to eat lunch with us this year!"

I always ate alone. Besides, my world had shrunk to a yellow pond of velvet petals that didn't include anyone else. "No, thanks." Another year of isolation, already set in stone.

The afternoon sped by, and the first day neared its close. I turned off the lights. The room quieted, and I began reading *Mrs. Frisby and the Rats of NIHM* aloud: Chapter One. The Illness of Timothy Frisby.

Lucy pillowed her head on her arms and watched me.

The intercom's squeal interrupted. "Teachers, please be sure students have the notes they need to take home." Mine were on my desk.

I smiled—en pointe.

The goats greeted me when I turned into the driveway. Before opening a can of soup, I made the first note in my journal for Cornell, 9/6 styro::$H2O$ & $C3H6O$=>POTD>D (on September

6th, I used Styrofoam, water, and acetone to set my students up to explore the first pattern of thinking, making distinctions). Essential question: What are the similarities and differences between the two fluids?

The sound of Joel's truck pulling into the gravel driveway surprised me as he hadn't let me know he'd be over. I reminded myself of the lesson I'd learned on my birthday: have faith in Joel's love. I leaned over the walnut stair railing to greet him.

He craned his head over the two paper grocery bags in his arms. "Okay if I stay?"

I double-checked his words. "You're going to stay with me? Tonight?"

"Yup. I'm staying tonight, clear until Sunday. I even brought a new mattress, so I can sleep."

"You brought us a new bed?" I pictured a king-sized, pillow-topped mattress with matching box spring. I forgot my promise to keep *It* under control, only meaning to hug my husband. As I launched toward him, my emotions exceeded my ability to control them. I squealed and hopped, then wrapped octopus arms around him.

The action spooked Joel, and he stepped away. "You stop it right now! I told you, I don't want any more drama."

I didn't understand at the time, but protecting himself from the unknown changes that had turned his wife into a raving, chaotic bitch was necessary and right.

"I'm sorry—really, Joel, I am." I made a binding decision to never be happy again because I made terrible choices with horrible consequences when I felt that emotion, and I no longer trusted it. Joel was more important than joy.

This would turn out to be a disastrous decision.

He set the groceries on the table. We settled into the living room, turned on my little TV, and opened our laptops.

"The roses were beautiful. I didn't think you'd remember."

"I remembered, Beth." He closed his eyes and then rubbed them as if he had taken off his glasses after reading for hours. "Do you? Do you remember me?"

What did he mean? Did I remember him? Joel looked like himself, but his words and actions were out of character. He hadn't hugged me or called me his girl since he arrived.

It was an odd question. "Of course! I always remember you."

Joel rose from the couch to put a pizza in the oven while I sat, stunned.

"Aren't you going to ask me how my day went, you know, the one at my new business?"

His new machining business was my arch enemy. Joel had started it shortly after our house sold, and it represented the burgeoning relationship with his new partners, a married couple who held sway over my husband's actions. The familiarity Joel shared with Hugh and Robin threatened me in the same way his family did.

They provided the escape hatch my husband needed, and I felt ostracized. Never mind it was me who had left.

Ashamed of myself, I inwardly chastised myself and then turned to face him. "How was your day?"

"See how you are? Beth, do you see? Who put the pizza in the oven? Who made you ask about my day?"

I didn't understand. I was no different on this day than any other. What was the anomaly? This was my first glimpse of his emotional dimension. To me, Joel was Joel, an even-tempered man, always in control, who didn't have moods that changed from moment to moment or feelings that got hurt. He was always fine.

In the early evening, Joel hauled his new twin-sized mattress up the stairs and assembled its frame next to mine. I spread a quilt over the two beds, trying to splice the parts into a whole.

⁂

The following day, I formally introduced Dr. Cabrera's first pattern of thinking to my students.

Distinctions
(identity and other)
What is __? What is not __?

While we explored the distinction between the mystery serums, my inner thoughts explored me. What am I? What am I not?

That evening, the television provided background noise while Joel worked on the books for his business. I journaled about my students' thinking. We spent a cozy evening and introduced no new cracks to our eggshell flooring.

Later, in the dark bedroom, Joel was falling asleep. I leaned over the divide between our mattresses. "Thank you for my roses."

"Beth, I will always make sure you have roses on the first day of school. I love you. Now, go to sleep."

Oh, God! I hadn't remembered to ask! "How was your day?"

His exasperation spilled out. "Shut up."

Mine spilled, too; I turned my back to him and cried.

During the next week, my students and I explored the second pattern of thinking.

Systems
(part and whole)
Does __ have parts? Can you think of __ as a part?

I brought in a collection of toys to disassemble. The thinking patterns' questions pushed us to consider the toys as assemblages of interconnected pieces as well as their connections with other things such as play, or someone's job, or Earth's natural resources.

My students applied their new knowledge to the mystery bottles while I poked around my memories. What was I a part of? What were parts of me?

That night, I paced on the landing waiting for Joel to come home.

As soon as he closed the downstairs door, I hollered down the stairwell. "How was your day?" Then, I put a pizza in the oven. Joel reminded me to take it out when he smelled the burnt crust. I filled more pages in my journal for Cornell, and Joel worked on bookkeeping. We slept on separate mattresses under the same covers.

On a Friday afternoon, I picked up a rotisserie chicken and a bagged Caesar salad at the grocery store, my version of cooking. Joel arrived late; the moon and the evening star lit the path from his truck to the front door.

"How was your day?"

"Great!" He chattered while he climbed the stairs. "I made plans. We're going out to dinner with Hugh and Robin tomorrow."

"I don't want to."

Our conversation continued in the kitchen. Joel's tone became sharp. "Look, this is important to me."

There was an ultimatum attached, even though he didn't say "or else."

He let me stew. "We'll leave at six o'clock. While we're with them, don't you dare say anything about bacteria or Dr. Margulis. I don't want to hear Dr. Cabrera's name, either. It's my turn to be important. Do you understand?"

Dr. Margulis, an award-winning evolutionary biologist, had been my mentor before I met Derek. Her views of the microbial landscape changed my perspective of the world. One quote summed it up: *Life didn't take over the world by combat but by networking.* My usual conversation amounted to trying to convince everyone that nature wasn't fundamentally red in tooth and claw; instead, it was interdependent. What was left to say?

Fear immobilized me, breathing down my neck like a draught of night air. I didn't want to meet new people. Even in ordinary circumstances, orienting to unknown personalities caused anxiety. The stakes were high, and I faced a real-life nightmare: Joel offered me a chance to move forward with him by introducing me to his new partners, and I didn't have a thing to talk about except science.

≈

We met Hugh and Robin at an exclusive Italian restaurant near the ocean. My eyes swept the dining room to get a first read on an unfamiliar environment. Glints of light reflected by myriad varieties of gems interested me more than any of the people who wore them. The tables resembled bushes lit by fireflies.

Robin rose to greet us. Her crepe top paired with skinny jeans and spiked heels contrasted with my Ann Taylor suit and comfortable pumps. The mask I wore to greet parents expressed delight at meeting her.

Hugh and Joel fell into a discussion about metals, tooling, and machine feed rates. Robin ran her eyes over my suit, not bothering to hide her evaluation. "I know; I'll take my new best friend shopping. I like the look of heels with jeans, don't you?" She glanced down at hers.

What, in the name of God, just happened? I was her best friend? For heaven's sake, no one in their late fifties needed to try on skinny jeans and heels for the first time, especially under the guidance of someone in their mid-forties who wasn't rocking *the look* as well as she thought.

After the server cleared our plates, Robin held out her diamond ring, arching her fingers to show it off. Blue light edged the stone; it was the kind of diamond that spoke of privilege, arrogance, and power. "When the shop floor hits $100,000, I'm trading up. This one is only two carats; I want at least three."

I arched my hand, too, my finger encircled by a simple gold band, and served my only winning comeback of the evening. "I wouldn't change a thing."

By the time we drank our dessert liqueur, I knew Robin liked her whiskey neat, and she swallowed.

Joel had turned into as much a stranger as Hugh and Robin. My Coors Light guy swirled and inhaled the aroma of wine before tasting it; he laughed at dirty jokes and spoke with innuendo.

Hugh and Robin stepped outside for a cigarette. Joel, who had quit twenty years earlier, joined them, leaving me behind to stew with a dichotomy. I felt superior, yet I was the one lacking and alone.

Please don't make me climb into a box of your-size-view-of-me.
Let my limitations be my own, not ones imposed on me; and
let the corners be sky blue, not dingy, cardboard brown, and
let me run and play upon the hills alone if playmates can't be
found. I'll bring you all back rainbows and great armfuls of joy,
but please, don't put me in your box; it's really not my size.
—Arden Georgi Thompson

Rising to the Bottom

In October, I stopped sleeping. Instead, I journaled, filling one spiral notebook, then another, and another, recording classroom observations and spinning subsequent plans. My racing pen couldn't capture the river of words that formed and then evaporated to make room for the next.

My frenzied scribbling held deep meaning for me. *Which fungal network supported the trees whose shavings were in the pencil sharpener, and what words would be written as the pencil's newly freed graphite grated against paper? Shavings to shavings, carbon to carbon.*

Teaching and learning tyrannized my life. During the extra hours I gained from not sleeping, I rewrote my curriculum, infusing the patterns of thinking into every set of directions, every prompt, and every project I used in the classroom.

My students worked on the same tasks as all the other fourth-graders in the district, but they used a robust set of tools to complete them. Success bred success, and a culture of independent learners emerged.

I often stood outside my doorway watching busy children. That's where the language specialist found me.

"I have a piece of Mackenzie's writing. She said she wrote it herself. Would you take a look?" She handed me a stapled sheaf of battered papers.

"Oh, that's her Titanic project. It turned out great, didn't it?" I flipped through curled-edge papers and giggled. "Did you read about the chicken that escaped from steerage?"

She put her hand on her hip and narrowed her eyes. "Mackenzie can't write like this. What are you trying to do?"

I wasn't trying to do anything; I had already accomplished it. I handed Mackenzie's story back to the specialist. "You are welcome to visit anytime; Mackenzie would love to show you ThinkBlocks."

I wondered who taught the *specialist* to think of Mackenzie as incapable.

⁂

Alex, a boy with a Tom Sawyer swagger and a lisp, had advanced to my fourth-grade class without an ounce of effort. He preferred to hide under his desk and read as often as he could. His rolled sweatshirt served as a pillow. I'd tap my teacher's finger on his chair, and Alex would rise to put on a good show of being busy, then corkscrew to the floor again. He had never met a teacher who taped seventh-grade math problems over the ones in his fourth-grade math workbook.

Alex ignored his assignments. "I can do the math, you know."

I tapped my finger on his amended workbook. "Show me."

"I'm bored."

"Only boring people get bored."

Alex sulked until recess.

Early the next morning, Mr. Blanchard knocked on my door. "Did you tell a student he was boring?"

I wanted to lie and tell him I'd done no such thing.

He rolled his eyes. "I'll speak with Mrs. Aldon. Don't do it again, even if you're right." Then, he pulled up a chair and sat down. "Lucy's math scores have improved dramatically. May I talk with you during your planning period?"

"Yup. The kids are off to art; give me a minute." I escorted Room 403 to their class, then returned to find Mr. Blanchard studying the ThinkMaps my students had created.

He turned to me as I entered. "I have questions about Lucy's test scores. Where's her workbook?"

I was so glad I had fished it out of the trashcan on the first day of school and tucked it safely in my bottom desk drawer. I retrieved it, feeling I betrayed Lucy's privacy. Its pages were empty, except for my notes and colorful ink stamps. "I make a double-sized copy of the page for her and cut it apart, so she sees one problem at a time. I pick two she has to try, and the rest are challenge-by-choice."

Thankfully, Lucy was a desk-stuffer. I pulled out photocopied math problems, one crumpled slip of paper after another, complete with Lucy's peculiar notations and correct answers. "When she solves one of these, I write the date in her workbook, and she gets to stamp it."

"So? Am I to believe a photocopier made the difference?"

"No, no, getting the problems one at a time relieves some of her anxiety. She isn't confronted by what she can't do or how much more is waiting." I walked over to the bulletin board and removed her ThinkMap. "Look, this is the other reason big paper helps. She needs more room to work because she thinks about numbers as doubles."

He took the map from my hand and studied it. "I don't understand."

"She keeps track of numbers using a stair-step method. Look. See how she's written numbers at different heights? She's doubling. She sees ones, twos, fours, eights, and sixteens like we see ones, tens, hundreds, and thousands. Each stair-step represents a double."

"You can see that?"

I nodded. "See, here?" I pointed to a distinction square that held nested system triangles connected by a relationship loop labeled *double up*. "One doubles up to two, two doubles up to four, four doubles up to eight, so ten is three double-ups and two more."

"I don't get it." Mr. Blanchard retrieved the document from my hand. "This is what you are doing for Dr. Cabrera at Cornell?"

"Not the doubles, that belongs to Lucy. But teaching her how to externalize her thinking? Yes, that is for Cornell. You're holding a diagram of the way Lucy thinks about numbers. She's a good mathematician but she's been told that she was wrong so often, she believes it. She hasn't figured out place value, but her number sense is strong."

The dynamic and stern administrator looked at the poster on my wall, Dr. Cabrera's four simple patterns and guiding questions.

Making Distinctions
(identity and other)
What is __? What is not __?

Systems
(part and whole)
Does __ have parts? Can you think of __ as a part?

Relationships
(Action and Reaction)
Is __ related to __? Can you think of __ as a relationship?

Perspectives
(Point of View)
Can you think about __ from the perspective of__?

"Why don't you come in during math? Lucy can explain it better than me."

Soon, Mr. Blanchard could add and subtract with doubles.

Lucy checked out multiple sets of ThinkBlocks from the classroom library and worked on division.

In September, Lucy had started fourth grade withdrawn, and Alex had strutted in behind her. A month later, they entered into a peculiar partnership and took to working together on the floor. Each solved an amended set of math problems using ThinkBlocks and laughed like kookaburras when they figured them out.

At home, October was all about promises. I had promised Joel to keep *It* under control. Two months had passed since my birthday shopping spree and purchase of the turquoise Frigidaire. I didn't disclose those indiscretions to him, although I doubt I fooled him for a second.

Joel seldom went back to his apartment after bringing the new bed to mine. Over time, his possessions migrated to my apartment. By day, Joel spun metal with Hugh while I explored interesting ideas with students at school. He worked on his bookkeeping at night while I wrote in my journal. The TV droned in the background.

Until it became excessive, journaling seemed benign. Capturing snapshots of students' thinking to take with me to Cornell was a concrete goal and, to me, one of great worth. I felt industrious, assured, and ambitious. I would put my pen down after three o'clock in the morning and curl up on my mattress beside Joel. During the few hours I slept, I dreamed about patterns of thinking.

On a mid-October evening, Joel came home from work. I asked him if he'd had a good day machining metal.

He kissed me and plopped on the couch to take off his work boots. "I told Hugh and Robin we'd meet them at the inn."

The Inn, constructed in the early 1800s as a private home, boasted an award-winning menu and four-star hotel accommodations. Its "haunted heritage" made it unusual and noteworthy.

"We just saw them yesterday. We can't afford to keep going out."

Joel shrugged his shoulders. "Hugh's paying."

I changed out of my teacher clothes into different teacher clothes. "I have nothing to wear."

"You're fine."

I couldn't figure out the interrelationship between my husband and this new couple who had dropped into my life. They made me wary, and I attributed my discomfort as a reaction to personalities who pushed my buttons. I wondered, though, why were Hugh and Robin suddenly Joel's best friends? And why would someone like Miss Robin clamber for my attention?

On the surface, there was a friendship between them, but I was convinced the bedrock of the partnership was money. The equity from our house's sale combined with Michael's needs and his hopes was the ace of diamonds in Hugh and Robin's four-card straight flush. It was Joel's ready cash that Hugh spent setting his plans for a new business in motion.

That evening, Hugh and Robin sat at a table near the window, cocktails in hand.

"Hey, it's my best friend!" Robin rose from her chair to greet me with a hug.

I politely returned it. "Hi."

"Whatcha up to?"

"I'm collecting data about think—" Joel's glare stopped me short. Pinching a firehose shut would have been easier than silencing my mouth.

Halfway through dinner, Joel turned to me. "Hey, girl." He took my hand in his. "It's pretty stupid to keep paying two rents, don't you think?"

I slammed a mental wedge under the spinning wheel of burning-rubber emotions. Nodding was the only choice open to my overwhelmed brain. No more "staying over," Joel was coming back for good!

Robin said, "I knew you'd say yes!"

My eyes sought Joel's, looking for reassurance, while my mind's slitted eyes stared at Robin through cold hate. How did she know Joel would ask? And why would Joel choose to mend our fences in front of her? How dare she presume to know what I'd say!

Robin shoved a menu toward me. "This calls for drinks."

I could order one or make a scene. The menu had an entire page devoted to margaritas; I glanced at Joel for guidance.

Robin leaned toward me. "Just choose one already."

I ordered what I thought was a colorful slushie, a Sunrise Margarita.

Robin sat up straight in her chair. "Are you sure?"

"Of course."

My drink arrived with a sliced jalapeno pepper artfully stacked like hula hoops up the straw. I drank the layered capsaicin-spiked concoction, robbing my new "best friend" of the chance to ridicule me.

Robin dashed to a new topic. "This place is haunted; it was on TV. There was a cold spot on the stairs. Did you notice it when you came in? I think I walked right through a ghost."

"It *is* October."

"I got wicked goosebumps, you know, that feeling when someone walks across your grave." She shivered, then looked across the table at her husband. "I think we should have a Halloween party."

Hugh looked at Joel, then shrugged his shoulders. "Sure."

Tequila helped me ignore the line I had drawn in the sand between me and happiness. Excitement roiled and jubilation prevailed. "I've always wanted to go to a Halloween party!" I looked at Joel. His hackles raised—he knew overexcitement rippled under my skin.

"Take it easy. Remember, no drama. Sit down."

I didn't realize I had left my chair. I soared. Joel was coming home, and a dream-come-true Halloween extravaganza to boot. Making hand gestures helped me paint the scene. "Let's do red and black instead of orange; everyone does orange. I won't do gore, though, okay? We'll do elegant but spooky. Do you have a candelabra?"

I stood again to describe my ideas about how to turn Robin's house into a haunted mansion.

"Sit down," said Robin and Joel.

Robin didn't engage in choosing colors or a theme. "You decorate; I'll cook." Somehow, she knew of my penchant for ruining perfectly good food.

After dessert was served, Robin introduced a wonderful elaboration. "I know what I am wearing already. It's so sexy."

Costumes! I hadn't thought about costumes. Driving home, Joel held my hand while I chatted about every dress-up dream I ever had until we hit the second curve in the road. I rolled down the window, and Joel veered to the side of the road. The jalapeno burned worse on the way up than going down. Luckily, Robin wasn't there to witness my humiliation.

❧

On the day of the party, Joel parked on the road's shoulder, and we walked along Hugh and Robin's long driveway. A flood lamp lit a life-sized silhouette of a witch I had cut from plywood and painted black. She pointed her wooden finger at the front door.

Within, garlands fashioned from branches, dried weeds, and red roses festooned the stair railings. A silver-plate candelabra I'd found in an antique store held black candles. Gravestones lined the hall, bats hung in the windows, and blood-red punch was ready for dry ice.

I was in heaven; my long black skirt and flounced petticoat brushed the top of my heeled prairie boots. I dressed as an Old West schoolmarm, out on the town with her outlaw cowboy. Joel, outfitted in a duster coat and leather holsters designed to carry beer bottles, refused to wear cowboy boots.

Robin dressed as a pirate, wearing a tight red jacket with a sassy peplum shirt worn above a short skirt and thigh-high vinyl boots. Hugh was a pirate, too. He wrapped a long polyester scarf around his waist, sported a black eye patch, and drank from his private bottle of rum.

Fred and Wilma, a mad scientist, and Thing One and Thing Two arrived. For once, people wore their names. The event bewildered me; it was the first time the group of people around me didn't sit at a table, drink coffee, and play cards.

I didn't know any of the guests, but Joel seemed to be old friends with everyone. The music was classic rock and people drifted in and out of the living room and helped themselves at the bar. I didn't laugh at their lewd jokes and my apparent naivete made me a source of amusement.

Seeking escape, I went to find Joel. He smoked in the garage with Hugh. I thought the cigarette at the restaurant was a fluke. He taunted me with one, laughing at my appalled reaction. I approached with a mother's chiding look, and he flipped me off.

Joel was having the time of his new life.

I was hurt and mortified.

After midnight, most of the strangers called it a night and left. Three couples, though, remained. The men headed downstairs to play pool. Robin put Fleetwood Mac's *Tusk* concert on the TV and moved the coffee table against a wall.

The women began to dance; their sinuous and evocative movements extended invitations to be touched.

Robin held her hand out to me. "Come dance." She looked like a praying mantis with a reaching hand.

Scarlet-faced, I refused.

"We're just dancing." Robin's feigned innocence intimidated me.

Downstairs, pool balls smacked into each other, falling into pockets. Laughter, boos, and cheers rose and grew silent, then rose again. Bottles clanked, and someone accepted a bet.

Robin moved too close. "Come on, just do what we do. Pretend it's a sleepover."

"I've never been to one."

"Never been to a sleepover? That's bullshit."

My father's intolerance of social behavior had stifled mine. I'd never received an invitation to spend the night with giggly girls. I wondered what it would be like to be as confident and uninhibited as Robin and her friends.

I left them swaying to the music and opened the basement door, seeking Joel's protection.

On the wall of the finished downstairs room, a TV displayed larger-than-life porn. The blue haze of harsh smoke from reefers tasted as foul as it smelled.

I fled. The men erupted in laughter, and Robin smirked as I headed toward the hall. "Tell Joel I'm walking home." He had abandoned his trench coat on a bench in the hallway. I wrapped it around me and rushed out the front door, past the witch who seemed to point at me and laugh.

I walked down the dark, rural road toward its junction with a two-lane highway. Headlights slowed behind me. I knew it wasn't an ax murderer, but it might be someone wanting to take me back to that party. My prairie boots hurt my feet as I scurried along the graveled shoulder.

"Come on, girl, let's go home."

I stomped another hundred feet down the road. Joel followed; the truck's headlights illuminated the shoulder. I gave in, grabbed his outstretched hand, and squished my petticoat into the truck.

He drove a bit further and pulled off to the side. "You'd better drive." It was his turn to puke all the way home, and despite my love for him, a tiny bit of satisfaction surfaced each time he retched.

Moving from here to there quickly—no time
to dream or listen—going nowhere, fast.
—Arden Georgi Thompson

Barnes & Noble

When Joel told me he had volunteered our services to help Hugh and Robin stow the Halloween decorations in their shed, it was my turn to feel superior. I may not have rocked heels with my jeans, but I could organize anything—except the unusual chaos that infected my classroom. Surely, a person who couldn't fit Styrofoam gravestones into her shed needed my expert help.

The witch still pointed her finger toward the front door but had tipped so she rested against the bare branches of a forsythia bush. I edged past her arm to stand behind Joel as he knocked on the door.

I heard activity inside the house, but the door went unanswered. Joel rapped again. Robin opened the door, all smiles. She hugged him and held the door wide open for me. "No need to wait for us; just walk in next time."

Robin starred in a lousy B-movie I watched from between my fingers. The invitation to walk into that house, unannounced, unnerved me; any contact held the potential to slouch toward something seedy.

Hugh moved a bowl of fake fruit from the breakfast bar. He reached inside a cabinet stenciled with a grapevine border for a bottle of Bailey's to go in our morning coffee, then a second bottle of spirits for himself.

Robin opened a boxed coffee cake and busied herself arranging slices on a plate emblazoned with more grapes.

I didn't try to join in their long-winded conversation about milling metal and invoices and running parts to clients. They were one entity, and I was another.

Robin slammed her hand on the countertop. "Does that sound like something a good partner would do?"

I had missed it!

Joel sat, expressionless.

I mimicked everything about Joel except for his silence. Years of playground supervision poured forth. "Let's make sure we understand the problem before we try to solve it."

Hugh, a rooster with a squeaky lisp, spoke loudly. "We all get it. I don't need to fuckin' hear it again." He dashed the melted ice into the sink and poured more whiskey.

Joel's face offered no clues.

Hugh and Robin's bodies postured like boxers in a ring; hands stiffened and necks craned. Their tone indicated I sat inside a wasps' nest, and the wee beasties had their stingers out. Robin grabbed Hugh's glass, locked eyes with him, and slowly poured the expensive whiskey down the drain. "This one's going to cost you big time." Her venom went straight to Hugh's wallet. "I want to go to D.C."

She turned to me. "Want to go to D.C.?" She leaned back on the countertop behind her and glared at Hugh. "We both want to go to D.C."

I guessed I was going to D.C., a trip I'd longed to make.

Hugh threw up his hands and poured himself another drink.

Robin turned her attention to Joel. "You need time, too; this is perfect."

Robin and Joel smirked.

I needed the universe to pause. I hadn't officially accepted the invitation, and I wanted to explore the trade-off.

Joel turned to me and laughed. "Go, have some fun—it'll be good for you."

The conversation made no sense, and I felt like I had ducked out to get popcorn and missed the critical scene in a movie. Somehow,

Joel and Robin agreed sending me to the nation's capital would solve a problem.

"Aren't we going to do the shed?"

No one responded.

While I waited, I noticed several cracked floor tiles near the refrigerator. The silence tightened like a noose, so I broke it. "We came to clean the shed."

Robin glared at me for seconds in silence. "Fuck the shed. He owes this to me, and a lot more, I tell ya." She studied Hugh. "I'm going to St. Croix in the spring, too, you bastard."

Robin and I flew to Washington, D.C. on the Friday that began the long Veteran's Day weekend. Robin's pensive attitude made me wonder what was up. She watched the night sky through the plane's window and nursed an old-fashioned.

I didn't break her silence.

On Saturday morning, Robin rang my hotel room. "Fucking wake-up call woke me up."

I laughed, thinking she joked. "Ya think? Wake-up calls will do that."

"I feel like shit; I don't want to go anywhere. Will you be okay if I go back to sleep?"

"Food might help; I can bring you something."

Robin moaned. "I just want to sleep. Maybe I'll try dinner. Go without me."

I grabbed a bagel and coffee from a street vendor, an autonomous action foreign to me as I usually traveled with someone who would negotiate such transactions. I planned to visit the Smithsonian castle.

The colors of the city reacted to my presence and polished the grime from their faces. A streetlight bent in greeting. Knotted energy pulled apart my paradoxical core, at once terrified of being alone and ecstatic that I had no companion. Had I noticed, the feeling matched that burst of newly found independence I felt when I moved into my apartment.

November in Washington, D.C. differed from home. There was no bite in the air, and the leaves on the cherry trees that lined the National Mall were still brilliantly colored in autumnal tones of gold, peach, and burgundy. A black squirrel scampered under a bench and skirted a waterlogged pigeon feather on his way to a fence post.

Further along, I noticed a second feather whose sheen and form suggested it was carved marble. A third feather, barely visible under fallen leaves, glittered like alabaster crystals. A corner of heaven had fallen from beyond the clouds and blanketed the area. Park benches turned into upholstered settees. Leaves of satin and richly colored velvet littered the area.

I left the paved walkway and worked my way to the center of the grassy lawn, eager to lay claim to the feathers, I reached toward the ground. As I stooped, a heavy hand gripped my shoulder. Annoyed at being restrained, I craned my neck to identify the culprit.

I was alone with an untethered force pinning me in place. The nearest human being walked along the sidewalk. Invisible fingers moved the fabric of my jacket as a phantom hand squeezed my shoulder to reassure me I didn't imagine things.

A telepathic message without a beginning, middle, or an end communicated by the male entity, resonated as though he read a passage from the universe's secret archives. *Light is all around you.* He explained that even in the darkest hours, forms of light—gamma rays, X-rays, and radio waves—bathed me in brightness. I heard his voice, resonant and deep. *"Your eyes are not capable of sensing it; the magnitude of its presence would blind you. Light is best sensed with your heart. Know this: darkness is not real."*

People passed the feathers without noticing the beauty hidden beneath their dirty surfaces. Sorrow for those who couldn't use everyday light to see what was in front of them spilled from my eyes, and I wept for their misfortune.

Scattered before me, feathers of increasing complexity and other-worldly beauty led me helter-skelter to the museum's back entrance. The last vestiges of warrior angels filled the sky. Remnants of their armor roofed the silvery spires, and their wings dissolved into the hazy veil of clouds. The fallen feathers on the ground gave tangible proof of their presence. I realized the disembodied voice that spoke to me of light was that of an angel. I should have fallen to my knees but instead froze in place with wonder in my soul.

Once inside the castle, I climbed the stairs as if I were a novitiate ready to take a solemn vow. My vision sharpened. I noted tiny grains in the sandstone walls and scratches that revealed four layers of paint on the metal stair rail.

A security guard spoke to me. "Can I help you?"

His movement drew my attention to a poster hung in the alcove behind his desk that depicted the museum's original Children's Room. The similarity with my classroom was unmistakable. Vindication and validation of spending thousands and thousands of dollars on objects and experiences for my students hung on the wall. I sobbed as if I stood before an altar.

The guard rose from his seat. "Where are you from, miss?" He stepped out from behind his desk. "Miss? Miss, is there some way I can help you?"

I handed him my camera and explained I had followed an angel who led me to the poster. After taking several pictures, he returned my camera and helped me close my backpack's zipper because I couldn't.

The lower tip of a luminescent wing, dragging on the floor like a silvery-gray velvet train, slid past the adjacent gift shop's main entry. I bulldozed past the guard, then plowed through people as I gave chase.

The top of the angel's wings towered above the heads of museum visitors. I chased him through the maze of hallways. He paused long enough near an exhibition about paper engineering to allow my mercurial mind time to explore the idea of creating three-dimensional versions of ThinkMaps to take to Cornell.

The angel moved on and flowed up the stairs.

I followed. A Plexiglas version of a 1950s diner lit by red and turquoise neon lights invited visitors to explore science demonstrations in the upstairs lobby. An older woman dressed in a crisp, white lab coat leaned over the counter and engaged two teens in exploring double pendulums, a gem in the collection of unexpected events I used to start the school year—or when I had a migraine.

The sight made me envious. How dare another person usurp my limelight using my material? I turned my head and complained to the angel. "Do you see that bitch? She stole one of my favorites." I put my hands on the Plexiglas and yelled through the wall so the woman inside could hear. "Bitch!"

Several people moved out of my peripheral vision.

I fled down the stairs again, back to the gift shop, passing the guard coming toward me. The angel disappeared, but books on a center display featuring paper engineering replaced his presence. Some were simple pop-up books for children, while others were complex works meant for adults. I picked up one of each title, then one more as a Christmas gift, just in case an unexpected guest dropped by.

I chose a Smithsonian pencil for each of my students but thought that gesture lacking, so I picked out little plastic dinosaurs too. Then I noticed the erasers and thought of the gift bags Mrs. Westcott gave to her students. I added key chains to my pile because every fourth grader needed to be a keeper of keys.

From across the room, I spied earrings with amber cabochons set in sterling silver dragonflies. The insect represented transfiguration, and the amber stone possessed the power to freeze time—all of it held in place with silver metal reminiscent of angel wings. I restrained myself and chose only one pair. While returning to the register, a trilobite fossil caught my eye.

The guard talked with me while I completed my purchase, and he walked with me toward the exit. "Do you plan on coming again?"

"Not unless Robin feels better." I would have waved goodbye, but my hands were full.

I sat on a park bench and settled my shopping bags on the ground. A shiver ran along the bench, looking for a spine to run up. The angel settled his eight-foot frame beside me. His wings and longsword with a cruciform hilt passed through the solid wood as if the bench were a hologram.

"I'm tired."

"I know. It'll be all right." He faded away.

I was alone in Washington, D.C., with bags of books and a trilobite on my lap. I missed Joel and tried on my new earrings.

⁂

In the late afternoon, Robin and I walked along the mall to visit the memorials. She complained of a headache but felt well enough to drink herself through dinner. "What do you think those two are doing?"

"Nothing to worry about; Joel is there to watch Hugh."

We talked of nothing in particular and headed back to our rooms early.

When Robin and I returned home, Hugh picked us up at the airport and then dropped me off at my apartment. I was exuberant and ran up the stairs, shopping bags in hand. "Oh, Joel, guess what I found at the museum!"

"I don't want to know." He shifted his body away from me.

I knelt in front of him, thinking the books and bags were the problem. "The poster explained everything! Listen—"

"Shut the fuck up!"

Whatever had happened while I was under the castle's enchantment changed Joel.

I sank back on my heels. For the first time, I realized my husband recoiled from me, not my purchases.

That evening, I turned to my journal. Joel attended to his business. I held my breath and became as still as I could.

In the past, such knots had unraveled over time. Quiet days fooled me into thinking the crisis had passed. I put up our Christmas tree, confident we'd find each other again if I stopped my spending sprees. I applied for a second credit card so I could buy gifts.

Joel threw away his duster and the Stetson. He organized documents in the lockbox and sorted through clothes in his closet. The pile of gifts under the tree grew; I pretended to stay on budget.

When Joel asked me what I wanted for Christmas, I was aware it was one of those be-careful-what-you-ask-for moments. My credit card debt was out of control. I still needed to travel to Cornell and pay for a hotel room during the academy. After careful consideration, I asked for money. "Fifteen hundred dollars should cover it."

He scoffed. "You've got to be kidding. How about a sweater?"

"I don't want a goddamned sweater." Dogs got sweaters for Christmas. "Never mind, I'll ask Dad."

I seldom spoke to my father, so when I told him Dr. Cabrera had invited me to Cornell, he inflated it into a grandiose confabulation, and I didn't set him straight. "Just a loan, Dad. I'll pay it back."

A check for fifteen hundred dollars arrived a few days later.

On Saturday, I cashed it at the bank and drove to Barnes & Noble. I intended to buy a book about the Smithsonian for my father, a gesture of appreciation for his support.

When my boot touched the parking lot pavement, my perceptions shifted. I clutched the car door, taking a moment to acclimate to a new sensory landscape. Sounds changed their frequencies as if a shell had been put to my ear and repeatedly removed. The aural strobe made me dizzy.

An odd play of light turned the world into a negative image. From above, a cone of light shined into my eyes—I was an actress on stage playing to a darkened house. People froze in place, and cars in motion disappeared.

I looked about, a curious observer of an alternate universe. I walked, slowly and with majesty, toward the store's heavy brass-bound glass doors.

The double doors opened, maneuvered by people I knew to be there but couldn't perceive. The second set of doors likewise opened onto a ballroom filled with shelves of dancing books.

I was a human telescope. I scanned the shelves. The spine of every book appeared as a distinct entity. Every color stepped forward, showing off. "Me, me, me! Pick me!"

Living books slid forward, then were shoved back by their neighbors, who took their places. A thousand voices piped up.

"Me, me, me! I'm the one with relationships. Take me!"

"No, me. I have distinctions within. Pick me! Pick me!"

"I'm a book with a different perspective; ignore them!

A chorus erupted. "We are the parts; take us all!"

I stood inside the snow globe I held in my hand, watching myself and being myself at the same time.

Within the store, snow began to fall, backlit by the bright spotlight that shined from above. I raised my arms toward the black cloud ceiling and let the flakes fall on my face. They caressed with the delicacy of warm summer rain, but once they melted, they etched bitter trails across my uplifted face and hands.

I hurt beautifully.

The idea evolved of completing one last grand project with my students. We'd write a book for Dr. Cabrera, complete with an index of three-dimensional ThinkMaps. Books about complex adaptive structures—the weather, ecosystems, the brain, learning, and ant colonies—captivated me. I chose tangentially related books about the seasons, landscapes, psychology, and entomology. I bought adult versions for myself and children's books for my students.

I paid for piles of beautiful books with my dad's money, then carried the bags to my car.

I turned around and did it again. And again. Then, I returned for journals of every color to hold more writing, wooden chess sets for rainy-day recesses, colored pencils, bookends, and designer paper clips.

I handed over the rest of my dad's money to the store's till and charged the remaining balance to my new credit card. Room 403 was going to craft a masterpiece. Before returning home, I shuttled the bags of books from my car onto the school's concrete loading dock. I prayed the weather would hold until Monday morning and no thief would take notice. My brain was too maniacal to remember my master key would unlock the door so that I could take them to my classroom.

The receipts lay inside the bags. I ignored the voice inside my head that urged me to return the plunder; I needed them too much to take them back. I was frightened by my actions, but strangely exhilarated, my senses sharpened, my body tense.

On Monday, the janitor met me at the door. "I saw the bags when I did my building check yesterday. I thought they were yours."

I carried the first armload past him.

"Your poor husband."

I agreed with him but wouldn't let on. Poor Joel and poor me were involved in a chemical battle, played out in the theater of my gray matter. I had traded my last chance to be a wife for a pile of meaning-filled junk.

That evening, I told Joel about my shopping spree. I was sure I had a grip on myself. "All I need is a bigger bookshelf. This is the last, last, the very last thing I want forever. It can be my Christmas present."

The silence that ensued was different than the usual I'm-not-speaking spat. That night, he hugged the edge of his mattress while he slept. I was afraid he'd roll off onto the floor.

The stress interrupted the language center of my brain. I tried to spark a fight to settle our differences. "Spit it out, let's let what is be to be." I analyzed my stumbling language. Let's let what is be to be?

Joel echoed my words from months ago. "I called about an apartment." Christmas was two weeks away. I understood. He wasn't sliding through space and time as I had; he was disenfranchised and already gone.

"Don't go." I couldn't apologize because I was the wolf, the one who had caused harm. Please. Oh, God, dear God in whom I don't believe, don't let him go! I begged him in earnest. "Joel, please, I can't be alive without you."

"I won't go far."

But he was already too far away to reach.

Thoughts of suicide screamed at me, panicked imaginings of exterminating the pain of rejection, of escaping blame. On December 21st, I sent an email to Mr. Blanchard and assistant superintendent, Torey, informing them I would be out of the classroom for an unknown amount of time. A second email went to Dr. Cabrera, stating I wouldn't attend the leadership training.

Mr. Blanchard responded with a caring message reminding me to send a doctor's note to initiate my sick leave. He expressed concern about all my personal belongings as he couldn't guarantee their safety. He hoped I'd find a way to secure them elsewhere until I came back.

Dr. Cabrera acknowledged my regret and wished me well.

Dr. Grant wrote a note that I'd be out of the classroom for an unspecified amount of time. She patted my hand. "Let me know if you have any problems."

My children and friends helped me pack my personal belongings into boxes. Ingrid, a wise and dear friend, raised a ladder to the attic space over her garage, so we shuttled dozens of boxes filled with my classroom collection into her care.

The thought of watching Joel dismantle our bed when the time came for him to move sparked hysteria.

"Beth, come sit with me." He removed a throw pillow from the couch. "I'm sorry this is so hard for you. I think you should go visit Aunt Elizabeth for a while."

I'd had the same idea. My mother's younger sister, Elizabeth, floated on the surface of a glass half full, and she'd let me make my own decisions and then love me no matter what. Isolating in New Mexico with her would buffer me from having to witness Joel's departure.

We celebrated Christmas in strained silence. I tried to give him a gift, but he put it back in my hands once he'd opened it. The little box of credit cards cut into confetti was too little, too late.

Joel gave me a scarf and a ticket to Albuquerque. I wouldn't need to watch him while he carried his belongings away from the apartment we'd shared on the hill near the goats who loved Cheetos.

On Christmas Day, the eve of our physical parting, Joel sat with me on the couch. I curled into his arms, and he held me. "Joel, please don't go."

"It'll be fine."

*Now a thousand words with no meaning, a thousand
tasks with no goal. We are running from morning to
night into nowhere. We are losing our souls.*
—Arden Georgi Thompson

Leaving

The stars were still visible in the morning sky when I left home
on December 26th. I glued myself to Joel's side during the
drive to the airport. Our silhouette was that of lovers, but I was
saying goodbye.

Joel followed the signs to the deserted drop-off area for Southwest
Airlines. He stopped, then shifted into park, effectively ripping me
from his side. "It's time. Tell Aunt Elizabeth I love her, okay?"

Joel remained seated as I stepped away from the truck and rested
my backpack against my leg. My overstuffed, olive-green suitcase
waited in the truck bed, caught in an invisible tug-of-war between
two people who believed it wasn't their job to remove it.

The porter watched me wrangle the heavy bag to the sidewalk.
"I'll help you with that, ma'am." He intruded into my field of view
as I watched the truck's red taillights merge with traffic and distant
Christmas lights.

An automatic revolving door turned like a lonely carousel. The
repetitive sound of weather strips brushing along the glass enclo-
sure created another aural strobe, shushed waves that lapped against
my eardrums.

I stepped through the door's opening, traveled a complete revolu-
tion, and exited back onto the sidewalk. The skycap attempted to

help me a second time. Sure that a serial killer was swooping in for the coup de grâce, I fled to a safer entry into the airport terminal.

I was a three-year-old lost in a Mardi Gras parade. A ticket agent left the counter to help me print boarding passes and gave me directions I couldn't follow. She pointed to the person who had been in line ahead of me. "Just follow her."

A heavy-set woman carrying her knitting in a basket unknowingly led me toward security's maze of stanchions and webbed belts. A uniformed officer pointed to bins and my objects, guiding me through the screening process. My suitcase—cloaked by the miasma of my thinking—had dissolved from existence. There was no choice but to ignore the problem of its disappearance.

I lost sight of the bin carrying my backpack while tying my boots. Inside my brain, tension squealed like train wheels slipping on an iron track. The smell of coffee mingled with the sweet notes of pastry. That scent followed by aftershave, stale disinfectant, and the lingering odor of cigarette smoke on a passerby's leather jacket made me nauseous.

The flight numbers on the screen didn't match the seat number printed on my ticket. People rushed by, electric carts beeped warnings, and a mother scolded her toddler. My brain couldn't interpret their intermingled meanings. I swam, confused, inside a sea of scented sound.

I found the woman with the basket seated at a gate. She organized her knitting needles and yarn. "Excuse me, are you going to Albuquerque?"

"I am; my daughter's there." The woman flicked pink yarn onto her needle. "I want to get these booties finished before I meet my new little grandbaby."

"Is it okay to follow you onto the plane?"

"Of course." She smiled and patted the seat next to her. "Sit here. It'll be all right."

The airline boarded passengers. A tall, refined gentleman dressed in a turtleneck and blazer already sat in the aisle seat of my row. A second man, seated by the window, beat his thumb against the armrest and bobbed his head to the music his headset silenced. I belonged in the middle and wondered how I'd wedge myself between the two without taking out someone's eye.

Sadness blanketed my fear as if it draped over a casket with my body still fighting to live inside.

My backpack hit the man wearing the turtleneck and blazer, who was getting up so I could claim my seat. The person by the window ducked through my commotion to the aisle. I overheard him request a seat change.

The man in the turtleneck offered to help by stowing my backpack in the overhead bin. "Oh, don't!" I tried to grab it back. "Someone already took my suitcase."

"It'll be all right."

During the preflight inspection, the flight attendant spoke to the man in the turtleneck. "There are still a few empty seats."

I was grateful he stayed. For the duration of the flight, he and the flight attendant cared for me. I alternated between pulling my feet up to fold into a fetal position, crying, or bursting from my seat driven by an anxious need to pace, parsed by despondent surrender. They mopped up the water and coffee I spilled. The man read to me from a magazine, and we played tic-tac-toe while we crossed the central plains.

After we landed, I exited the concourse. Aunt Elizabeth greeted me. After a long hug, she stepped back and spoke with love. "Aww, you look like shit!"

The descending escalator to the baggage claim area fell like a roller coaster. Aunt Elizabeth steadied me as I stepped off onto the jelly floor, and then she searched through her purse for her keys. "Get your bag, and I'll meet you outside. We'll talk on the way home." She hugged me again. "Watch for a rusted white pickup."

The knitter cradled her new grandbaby while waiting for the luggage to fall from the chute.

My vaguely familiar olive-green suitcase slipped from the chute and traveled around the baggage carousel. How it had found its way to Albuquerque defied explanation. The man in the turtleneck and blazer rescued it and set it at my feet. "Are you going to be okay?"

"Yes, my aunt's here. Thank you. I know I made your flight miserable."

He held the door, and we exited the terminal together. I looked at his forehead, too ashamed to meet his eyes. "I'll always remember your kindness."

My aunt and I drove through Albuquerque's beautiful north valley, a sweeping vista of parched soil broken into irregular hexagonal shapes and windswept sagebrush growing twisted and low. Clumps of thickly branched cottonwood trees, some towering a hundred feet high, traced the dendritic drainage paths that channeled rainwater toward the Rio Grande.

My aunt's empathetic words turned to the nuts and bolts of daily life. "If you don't want to go back, you don't have to, you know. You can have the little bedroom all to yourself, but you'll have to buy your own food."

Aunt Elizabeth turned the truck onto 4th Street. "Now, if you think I'm going to put up with your outbursts, I won't. I'll kick you out. I've had enough of that shit in my life, and I'm not going to take it anymore, not even from you."

I blinked. Had I been giving her shit?

"We'll have rice and beans because that's all I can afford. I've got peanut butter, and the church dropped off some bread."

"Aunt Elizabeth, I've got money."

"That's okay, sweetie, we don't need it. Now, I can't give up my bed because my back hurts and the heater's broke, so it's cold. I have to work at the store. You can come in with me if you want, but you're not going to stay in bed and cry. There's a girl across the road that needs help, or there's a shed you can clean out back. Put your towels in the washer, I can't stand dirty towels, and you can use my shampoo, but not my lotion."

My aunt took a breath.

I wedged my elbow against the truck's window and rested my head on my fist. The alpenglow, a rosy, reddish light reflected from the Sandia Mountains' sedimentary rock, illuminated the horizon. My aunt reached over to pat my leg. "It'll be all right."

The empty platitude echoed. "Everyone keeps telling me that, and I think you're all a bunch of idiots." I hoped the angel would understand I meant no blasphemy.

Aunt Elizabeth bit her lip, and we finished the ride to her home in stony coldness. She lived in the back rooms of a decrepit adobe ranch house converted into an antique store during the 1960s. A *Closed* sign hung in the picture window, and a profusion of red geraniums grew in the battered, galvanized horse trough that flanked the store's back entrance. A blue door opened into a kitchen with a brick floor.

My aunt hung up her coat, then whipped maple syrup into peanut butter. "Go ahead, get settled; your room is across from the bathroom; it's the only one that works so make sure it's always clean; sometimes, customers use it."

A camping cot lashed into an ornate rusted iron bed frame sat against the bedroom's sage wall. She had turned back the white lace-edged sheet and vintage quilt pieced from raspberry and shades of mulberry. Two new thick towels appliquéd with tulips and a piece of chocolate waited for me on the pillow.

I returned to the kitchen, humbled by her generosity and comforted by her unconditional love. She opened a sleeve of saltines and arranged them on a delicate, scalloped-edged Limoges plate borrowed from the window display.

"Here, have as much as you want." We spread thick, satiny gobs of peanut butter and syrup on the crackers. The conversation was one-sided; Aunt Elizabeth told me everything I should do.

Albuquerque was a beautiful place in which to be devastated. Late that first night, I left the little bedroom to stand behind the chain-link fence that separated the shop's parking lot from the four lanes of traffic humming by, soon to pass over the broad, shallow Rio Grande.

Tractor-trailer trucks rumbled past, each followed by a draft of air. Every evening, I closed my eyes to discern their rhythm. They were my ledge, and I held my breath at its edge until the metallic smell of diesel exhaust ended my imagined jump.

On the day I should have been exploring ThinkBlocks in Ithaca, New York, the weather turned in Albuquerque. It snowed. That night, my woolen coat couldn't block the chill. Aunt Elizabeth was particular about her belongings, so I didn't dare rummage through her coats without asking. Instead, I sorted through the tower of linens and fabric she collected, picking out large tablecloths for extra covers.

From her bedroom, Aunt Elizabeth shouted, "Shake 'em! There's spiders in there! I can't give you my blankets, I worked hard for them and I'm cold. Take what you need, just fold them back up in the morning."

I examined my privileged life and shamed myself for not having the strength to overcome my fear of being alone like Aunt Elizabeth had. It was the dislike of myself that I feared most. I wondered if anyone would want me around again.

Every evening, I visited the fence that separated the store's parking lot from the busy street. The world seemed to be asleep. I imagined the drivers as simulacrums, clockwork men with clockwork hearts instead of ones that bled. Surely, they'd barely notice a thump.

Would I?

Who are you; who am I? Ourselves, or think-things created
by a thousand hearts and eyes? Plural beings or singular
mirrors? Dragons, angels, slain, or slayers? Who are
you, who am I? Can I see you before the I of me dies?
—Arden Georgi Thompson

Flame and Ashes

A few weeks after New Year's Day, I worked alongside my aunt dismantling the antique shop's holiday decor. Back home, my Christmas tree waited in the living room, each ornament frozen in time. Throughout its abandonment, its artificial branches had remained vibrant.

I existed in no-man's land. Aunt Elizabeth's little bedroom never became home, and I possessed nothing but clothes, an olive-green suitcase, a backpack, and a computer. Without Joel or school, I was untethered and alone.

One day, I decided it was time to return home. I needed to experience the void created by Joel's absence. If a witchy woman had been casting spells, I'd have asked her to set aside her obsidian wand and wave one carved from glowing moonstone to lift my heart. An infinitesimally small glimmer of hope wanted to feed Cheetos to the goats, brush them, and cry into their scratchy, dirty fur. I bought a plane ticket to travel back home.

On the third Thursday in February, the last one I'd spend in New Mexico, the skies clouded. Gray rainy days had always quieted my students, and on this day, I welcomed the muffled sounds and slower tempo of the traffic. The cadence of raindrops against glass windows was a ticking watch in the hand of a skilled hypnotist.

Aunt Elizabeth moved toward the storefront to flip the sign. "I'm closing the store today. Nobody'll be out in this weather."

We decided to spend the morning cooking, so we drove to a family-owned local market to buy handmade tortillas and fresh vegetables. By mid-morning, enchilada sauce simmered on the stove's back burner. The simmering smell of garlic, dried guajillo chilis, and fresh tomatoes hung so thickly in the air I could taste it.

I cleaned up the mess we'd made while Aunt Elizabeth dug through her closet, sorting through the old linens I had disturbed on the night it snowed. The rain stopped, and light from the window skipped across the red geraniums and illuminated the tabletop.

"Oh, my God! I found it!" Aunt Elizabeth pulled an old box of photos from the bottom of the closet. She carried it to the kitchen table. Most of the black and white photos were of people I'd never met, but some were familiar. I recognized my grandfather and grandmother. I didn't ask about the children posed as Bonnie and Clyde with cigarettes hanging from their mouths. My uncle T.W., the youngest brother and proud sailor, sat on the front steps of his mother's house, holding a Boston terrier and a bottle of 7-Up.

One faded Polaroid captured the time when Aunt Elizabeth had taught me how to rub a dandelion on my face to find out if I liked butter. Her laughing face and my yellow chin elicited a strong memory of a warm summer day when love was all around me. We were beautiful.

A newspaper clipping hid under the collection of photos. Yellow, brittle cellophane fell off when Aunt Elizabeth lifted the long section of folded newsprint. "I thought I threw this away." She pushed the pictures aside and set the clipping down on the table. Her finger smoothed the center crease. I read the headline from across the table.

Man Freed from Hospital Attacks Wife, Kills Himself. The old newspaper article reported that my grandfather had slashed his throat with a razor.

Aunt Elizabeth closed her eyes and told the story again. "I was four. Jenny Lee [my mother and Aunt Elizabeth's sister] shoved me under the bed and made T.W. get under too. There was blood everywhere, all over the kitchen. It got on me when Jenny Lee pulled me and T. W. out from under the bed."

The article stated my grandfather had been confined to the state mental institution for seven months and *was deemed by his psychiatrist to be fully recovered from bipolar disorder.*

Aunt Elizabeth and I leaned closer to read the newspaper clipping. *...Sheriff Elmer White disclosed that Mrs. Evans* [my grandmother] *had protested when told her husband was to be released. (She) emphasized that she didn't believe Mr. Evans has had sufficient time to be fully recovered from his mental illness and...would like for you* (the hospital) *to keep him a while longer to be sure that he is fully recovered. Mrs. Evans asserted that if he was returned now the sheriff's department would be held responsible for his actions. She went on to say he had threatened her and the children's lives if he ever returned home...*

Aunt Elizabeth's breath caught as she identified the discontinuity between her version of events and those laid forth by the newspaper reporter. She pointed to each word as she reread aloud. *A passing motorist, Arlan Morales, picked up Mrs. Evans and her three children and took her to a physician's office.* Aunt Elizabeth fiddled with the brittle tape. "Only me and T. W. were in the car. Jenny Lee didn't come with us."

I watched with fascination as her face changed with her shifting thoughts, then I reread the passage. It said three children rode with Mr. Morales, the passing motorist, but, according to my aunt, that wasn't true. The third child, the one wet with blood, did not.

Aunt Elizabeth backed her chair away from the table and sat with her eyes focused on a phantom car. "Jenny Lee killed my dad."

"I bet she did." I made the statement without a shred of doubt. A wave of cold washed through me, raising goosebumps and the hair on my head.

This, then, was my mother's secret. On the day she needed to protect what she loved, she was as strong as fire, and her act left her as fragile as the ashes left behind.

Different personalities ebbed and flowed beneath my mother's skin. Defeated Mom was lifeless; her body would drape across a chair or bed like discarded clothing. If Angry Mom appeared, her body still had blue eyes and honey-colored hair, but her skin tightened, and her eyes became those of a hunter. When this Mom was out and about, I was prey. She told me she'd kill me if I didn't sit in my little rocking chair like a good girl.

I believed her.

For one ethereal, unforgettable morning, my *real* mother, the woman who wasn't hurt and could love and laugh appeared.

On that day, the Montana sun had silvered the dirt and made the heated air shimmer. My mother said it was hotter than a firecracker, and the buzzing grasshoppers agreed. The meadowlarks were silent, concealed behind the limp leaves of chokecherry trees. The algal paint that had slickened the boards that bridged the irrigation ditch in the spring curled into dried lime-green rime frost. The snails closed their opercula.

After breakfast, my mom suggested I should water the grass. For her to put four-year-old me in charge of the garden hose wasn't just unusual; it was downright strange. Watering the grass was usually the job of the sprinkler, but not on this day. It was to be me, me, me! I held the screen door open long enough to cross the threshold. The door slammed behind me.

"Don't slam the door."

The outside spigot, crowned with a broken handle and robed with green grass and yellow goat's beard flowers, poked through the garage's back wall. Tedious seconds ticked by while I waited for my mother to attach the hose, stretch its length to the front yard, and then unkink it before finally relinquishing the magic nozzle to me.

She went inside to tidy up.

I was adept at sprinkling. I could make the water shoot higher than the chokecherry tree's highest branches or loosen the nozzle so I could be the umbrella and let the water fall on me like gentle, cold rain.

The screen door slammed behind my mother as she crossed the threshold to stand on our concrete porch. So softly, in front of my eyes, a lovely lady surfaced to animate my mother's skin. She walked to the edge of the garage as if she were a princess being presented at a ball.

"Come look." She was down on all fours, gazing at doodlebugs' holes. "See the fairy wells?"

Curiosity piqued, I set my trepidation aside. I had never seen a fairy's well. I bent down, hoping to glimpse a wee-winged girl winching up a tiny bucket filled with miniature water. The hose misbehaved and soaked my mother's perfectly ironed white shirt. As I flailed for control, water blasted her hair and face. My bottom tingled with the expectation of the spanking sure to follow.

Instead, she laughed. My mother laughed! She reached toward me and took the hose from my hands. I lowered my eyes in shame and waited for her to teach me a lesson. Instead, she showed me how to fill the fairies' wells by letting the water drip down her fingertips into the dusty cone-shaped burrows.

We painted the walkway dark gray. Then, after the dandelions drank their fill and after each blade of grass was decorated with a rainbow held in a droplet at its tip, she went back inside. The beautiful lady who had tried on my mother's skin was gone.

I never saw her again.

Tears meandered down my aunt's weathered cheek. "They took Jenny Lee away to live with Belle. Your momma never came back. I wanted her to come home and get me." Belle was the eldest sister who lived in Amarillo, Texas, the city of my birth.

Time passed like the flow of melting rock. I wanted to comfort my mother, to absolve her beleaguered soul, and watch her lift her face to the sun.

It was easy to imagine Sheriff Elmer White and a kind man being in the right place at the right time to lead a sixteen-year-old blood-covered girl to safety, to take her away from circumstances that could have branded her a murderer. Good people in small towns did things like that sometimes.

Aunt Elizabeth snapped off the stove's burner. "I want to go there before you leave; I can't do it alone."

We put the sauce in the refrigerator and drove to San Raphael, a little more than an hour's drive from the city. I wanted to visit the graveyard and touch the only remaining traces of the people whose images rested in the box. I expected a town filled with haunted houses surrounded by tumbleweed gardens, but it was indistinguishable from any other small town in New Mexico.

We asked for directions at the Conoco station. Then, we stopped at the local market and I bought a bouquet of daisies with the hope we'd also find the lost grave of the youngest of the four sisters, Little Birdie, who died at age two.

According to Aunt Elizabeth, her sister had died of pneumonia. Mom's story varied: sometimes, Little Birdie had disappeared, sometimes, she had drowned. In other versions, my mother told me her baby sister had been taken away. No one in the family knew or would tell what had happened to her or where she rested.

A metal arch welcomed us to San Raphael Memorial Cemetery. We found my grandfather's headstone and Belle's grave, but there was no trace of the baby. I started to believe something sinister had happened. Was she buried somewhere in the bean field like my mom had once said? There was more secrecy about Little Birdie's death than there was about my grandfather's.

We drove away, somber and silent. I still carried the wilted daisies.

Aunt Elizabeth broke the silence. "I want to drive by." The old farmhouse was near, surrounded by an open field of clotted dirt, still clear and ready to be plowed. We drove closer until my aunt's body shook, forcing her to park the truck. "That's where my dad sat with his .22. He'd shoot at the tractor if Stephen's rows weren't straight."

I'd heard this story as well. Uncle Stephen, the oldest boy, ran away from home, preferring to hide in the ditches with the rattlesnakes than face his dad. He had made his way to Albuquerque and enlisted in the Air Force.

She whispered and pointed to the field that still surrounded the back of the dilapidated farmhouse. "That's where the watchers stood."

The watchers were armed neighborhood men who'd stood in the field, protecting my grandmother and her children each night after my grandfather's release from the hospital. I could almost see their ghostly figures standing like scarecrows with shotguns hanging by their sides.

We were so involved in reconstructing the past that the rap on the car window hit our hearts like a defibrillator.

A nosy older woman knocked on the driver's side window, shielded her eyes from the glare, then touched her forehead to the glass. "Just checking to be sure y'all all right."

Aunt Elizabeth nodded and rolled down the window before gesturing to the house. "I used to live there and am just showing it to my niece."

"You one of the Evans girls? I remember your family! Which one are you?"

The stranger invited us to sit on her porch and drink iced tea. I offered her the wilted daisies; she took them inside and put them in a vase. "They'll perk up in a bit." She and my aunt talked, one story leading to the next, the way stories do while you're chatting on a porch and drinking iced tea.

My aunt probed into the past. "Do you remember the watchers?"

A subtle shift in tone and body language indicated Aunt Elizabeth's words touched a sore spot. The woman remembered— her dear late husband, Sheriff Elmer White, had led them.

Elmer White. That name appeared in the news article. ...*Sheriff Elmer White, John Matton, and Harold Rood went to the Evans home. They found Evans dying, his throat cut, and a razor blade nearby in a pool of blood. He died a few minutes later.*

"When the hospital released your daddy, everyone was scared. It was the first time I locked my door. We all knew he was going to kill someone. That day, the men had already been out there every night for five days, ever since he was released." She pointed a rheumatic finger to the field. "They all had shotguns, guarding y'all. That mornin', it all happened so fast. The men had come in for breakfast and then they had to go to work." She reached out to pat my aunt's hand. "I'm so sorry, honey. I had trouble sleeping for weeks."

My aunt wanted her memory validated, even though she didn't want to hear the truth that would implicate my mother. "Did Jenny Lee leave with Mr. Morales?"

"Oh, no. Elmer took her down to his office. I brought them down some supper later. Rood was a watcher too; you should talk to him. He lives down the road, right after the cattle gate."

The ice in our glasses had melted. We said our goodbyes and exchanged the expected pleasantries. We had no courage to talk with anyone else. What more could they say? Aunt Elizabeth and I returned to the truck and drove back to the city.

Once home, until it was time to leave for the airport to catch my flight a few days later, my aunt isolated herself by making me a throw pillow out of soft vintage velvet, some of the scrap material she had rescued from a dumpster. It was her way of saying goodbye.

Little bird, do you sing because you will
or because without song you'll die?
—Arden Georgi Thompson

Letting Go

I traveled home locked inside a semi-permeable bubble. An hour into the flight, a hand passed me coffee, then appeared again to collect the empty cup. A body climbed over my knees, reminding me I needed to relieve myself too.

Aunt Elizabeth's jewel-colored pillow lay in my lap as if it were an inconsequential souvenir, so no one could witness how badly I needed it. More damned tears fell, blurring the turquoise, emerald, and amethyst colors. The pillow changed into a scrying bowl, and as I stared, I watched my mother's image grow old. I said the words aloud, making the stranger in the adjacent seat turn away. "It's all right, Mama." I forgave her and begged God in whom I did not believe to do so as well. What I really wanted was for her to forgive herself.

During the late-night descent into Portland, the sight of traffic made my neck muscles constrict. One of those tiny beads of light might be Joel racing to meet the plane. When we had talked on the phone before my flight, he'd made it clear he felt put upon by my request for a ride. I imagined he'd changed his mind.

The hydraulic whine as the landing gear lowered signaled our approach to the airport. Minutes later, the plane taxied to a stop at the terminal. The father of a sleeping child stepped into the aisle while the mother shouldered her toddler, waking him. His sleepy eyes opened with every jostle. He grinned at the flight attendant, then buried his face in the hollow of his mother's neck.

At the end of the concourse, the boy's eagle eyes spotted Grandma waiting behind glass doors. He kicked to be let down, bulldozed through the crowd, and left Mom and Dad to manage the stroller, car seat, and carry-ons.

I wanted to be that child, to be swept up in Joel's arms. When I stepped onto the escalator and scanned the crowd again, he wasn't there. Had he stood me up or forgotten? Should I hitchhike home? Rent a car? In a panic, I chided myself to act normal, for Christ's sake.

My heart soared imagining Joel's absence to mean he was off to buy roses and would embrace me at any minute. But no, he waited near the baggage carousel. His stance, one foot on the floor and the other wedged against the wall, exuded arrogance that demeaned him and demonstrated intolerance that demeaned me. He didn't step forward in greeting.

Behind me, the little boy slept in his grandmother's arms while the luggage slid onto the conveyor belt. I set my jewel-colored pillow and backpack on the floor near Joel and moved to retrieve the heavy, olive-green suitcase myself.

In late February, brittle, bare-limbed trees contrasted with the green swellings on New Mexico's cottonwood branches. For the first time, my husband didn't protest that the below-freezing temperature was too cold for his girl and tell me to wait while he brought the truck around.

Joel's six-foot frame covered ground much more quickly than mine.

I trudged behind, burdened by my backpack, pillow, and suitcase, which tipped over each time it hit a crack in the sidewalk.

His patience snapped. "Here, give me that." He pulled my suitcase past the concrete pillars to the second floor of the parking garage, then heaved it into the truck bed. He paid for parking, then drove down the access road. "Hungry?"

I wanted to sit in a restaurant with him for hours, holding onto his hand, but he wouldn't entangle his fingers with mine, so why bother? "No, I've got food in the freezer."

At home, the truck's headlights glinted across the barbed-wire fence. A light shined in the upstairs window. Unshoveled snow covered the path to the door. Silence. No goats charged the fence begging for treats. "Where are they?"

"How should I know?"

The void threatened from behind the front door, an emptiness vaster than Joel's abandonment. I couldn't summon an adult thought and was afraid. Joel was my container; he defined my edges and held me together. I begged him to stay with the intensity of a child calling out in the night. "Come in with me, please; I can't do this."

His jaw clenched, and his face blanched white. "Now you know how I felt when you left."

My eyes widened in surprise. I thought he knew our separation had been an unexpected calamity. Hearing his comment made me realize how deeply I'd hurt him. The weight of that knowledge knotted my guilt firmly into place.

He backed out of the driveway, promptly pulled back in, and removed my forgotten suitcase from the truck's bed. He set it on top of the snowbank. Then, he was gone.

I stopped twice while climbing the gallows stairs to my apartment, then opened the door. The light in the living room came from the Christmas tree's white lights, which Joel must have plugged in to illuminate my way.

The quilt remained undisturbed; Joel had flung it back, taken his twin mattress and box spring down the stairs, then pulled them back into place. A circular area around his missing recliner lay bare, and beyond the emptiness, my chaotic mound of notebooks, pens, and paper reached from the couch toward the Christmas tree.

I unplugged the tree's lights and slept on my half of the severed bed.

In the morning, I decided to lie next to the light all day. Time passed without features to mark the hours. After the sun dipped below the horizon, I explored my home like a wraith, finding where Joel had pickpocketed items: a missing toothbrush, a few plates, one towel, and a picture taken from the hall. Each object's insignificance made its loss more prominent.

The second time I woke, my head hurt. I threw up on my bed covers and cared enough to bundle the mess to the floor, then grabbed an extra blanket from the closet and cried myself back to sleep.

A car pulled into the drive, and someone rapped on the downstairs door. "Mom? It's me, Allison."

I yelled at her, hoping my voice would carry through the old plaster walls. "I'm okay. Go home, Ali."

She climbed the stairs, then quietly sat next to me on the half-bed. "I'm sorry this happened to you."

My nose had bled while I slept. Allison removed the pillowcase, wrapped the pillow in a towel, and slid it into a clean case, then covered my hand with hers. "Sean and I need you to be okay. We're worried about you, Mom."

When I didn't answer, she picked up the stinking pile to launder at her house. She paused at the head of the stairs. "People go on after bad things happen, you know."

Days passed, and Allison visited again. This time, I didn't hear her car or footsteps on the stairs. She appeared out of thin air, standing in the doorway between my bedroom and the kitchen. She sat next to me. "Take a shower and eat. I put a shepherd's pie in the fridge." She rose from the bed. "I won't be back until you take care of yourself."

Wise child. My thinking was darkly manipulative. I wanted to force others to rescue me, and she set a firm, caring boundary between herself and my despair. She picked up the basket with my clean bedding and placed it on the kitchen table. "Call me. I wrote down my number; it's by the phone."

How did she know I no longer remembered it?

Allison closed the bedroom door behind her. I wanted her to stay and be the mother for a while. Her footsteps sounded as tiny as they did when she was two. The sound of her car's engine faded into the distance. She left me as frightened as an abandoned child in a refugee camp.

Inside the bathroom, a clown's death mask stared back at me from the mirror. Three days of crying left puffy, blue bruises around my eyes and blood-stained mucus smeared from my nose to chin. The water heater couldn't keep up with my demand that it supply a hot waterfall for me to hide behind for eternity.

My body craved food, so I licked spoonfuls of peanut butter and opened a can of root beer, forgetting Allison had put dinner in the fridge.

⁂

It was time to dismantle our Christmas tree. Each ornament I removed pushed me to reevaluate my situation. Had Joel come back because he was saving money for his new apartment? What had Hugh and Joel been up to while I was in D.C.? Had he stopped by to light the Christmas tree as an act of comfort or was it a stab in the back? Perhaps he hadn't unplugged them in the first place. Was there no deeper meaning?

I had no answers.

After carrying the boxes of ornaments and lights out to the barn, I dusted, vacuumed, and wrote checks to cover the bills. Then, as if I were leaving a note for a friend, I took an old piece of stationery from a box I had saved since high school. *I am doing this, so you know how sorry I am.* That was all I knew to write. Sorry was a word like *love* or *thank-you*; only the brain stringing the letters together knew their true meaning.

After the sun set, I organized my jewelry box and tried on my baby ring. The tiny engraved golden circle barely fit on the tip of my little finger. Joel's first Christmas gift to me, a small sapphire necklace, was secure around my neck.

Outside, the broken moon, stripped of its color, revealed its leaden heart. No street lights illuminated the long road. I picked my way, using the contrast between the moon's dull, gray reflected light and the dark asphalt as my trail. A keening cry from a night bird echoed my state of mind.

There was a mysterious boundary within the woods, thinner than a thread. On one side, the forest whispered; when I crossed it, the traffic droned. The delicate hum of engines became muscular and fierce as I closed in on my destination.

The streetlamp at the intersection of the highway and the road haloed me. I walked on the narrow shoulder, considering how far I should be from the intersection so the feigned accident would appear to be nothing more than a foolish slip and fall.

Spikes of dramatic emotional upheaval flattened into simplicity. I focused on the mechanics of being in the right place at the right time.

When I stepped across the white line, it was a decision like flinging the covers off on a cold morning or stepping out of a hot shower. I just did it. The act happened inside an emotional vacuum.

The driver wrenched the semi into the other lane, its air horn screaming mad. I hunched my shoulders to protect myself from the draft, tucked my chin tight to my chest, and squeezed my eyes shut to shield them.

The game of ring and run at death's door ended.

I was alone on the road, cold and fearful of what remained. One leg's bones turned to cartilage, and with my tremulous thigh still afraid, I stood on the other leg until the weakness passed. Emptiness surrounded me when I moved off the asphalt.

The driver deserved more than an apology, but how could I extend it? He drove on.

Returning home was an uphill climb. The forest silenced itself as if a finger dampened its vibration; it presented itself as unperturbed, alien, heartless. I used my scarf to swipe at tears and snot, but the cheap acrylic yarn couldn't absorb them, so they smeared.

The moving air evaporated their moisture, leaving behind shiny traces of salted mucus. My coat wasn't enough of a barrier against February's wind.

An owl called, and its mate responded.

When I opened the door to my apartment, the warmth of my apartment stung. I called Joel to ask, once again, for his help. "I'm scared, Joel. I almost left."

He knew my meaning; he'd heard the words *I'm going to leave* many times. "Stay where you are; it'll be okay."

Surely, he would come, hurrying up the stairs. The dial tone talked with me while I imagined leaning into his strength, his calmness, holding on for dear life.

Quick footsteps. A rap at the door, which I ignored, hoping my husband would know to come in without permission. A second knock, then the door opened, not by Joel, but by a police officer. I listened to the shape of his words and agreed with everything he said because it was futile to do otherwise.

Red lights. Multiple thuds. Hard bumps with a metallic ring. The paramedics expected me to climb onto the gurney.

I refused.

They won.

The ambulance carried me down the same road I had just ascended, retracing each meandering turn. We stopped at the street light marking the intersection of the road and highway. I looked at it through the small window in the ambulance's back door. I had just been there and wished the journey would end.

The archangel emerged from the confines of the street lamp's slender pole, his face hidden behind his massive wings. In the smallest unit of time that exists, he communicated a second sacred message. *Love is light.* Again, a library of information poured into my brain's convolutions. *The fundamental element of the universe is not quarks but bundles of congealed love. Mask your mathematical mind and feel the equation. E=mc^2 is more than a conversion formula. Find equivalency. E is weightless love that balances the heaviness of m, the hopeless heart.*

During that smallest speck of time, the angel allowed me to explore my mind. I asked him a question: Does this mean zero and infinity are the same?

It does.

How can that be?

You look for boundaries that do not exist. You seek love as if it were absent. Atoms are made from congealed love; your emotions are love; your spirit is love. Remember, the darkness is not real.

My sense of self widened to include the chair. I was the chair, and the chair was me. The hospital room and I became one, then the ceiling disappeared. I spread out toward infinity, subsuming the planets, the night stars, the galaxy, and beyond.

I don't know how long the universe cradled me. I was everywhere at all times, not somewhere seeking to be someplace else.

What had happened? My question interrupted the experience. I snapped back into my skin, alone on a gurney.

*Some of the finest things I've ever done were not
preplanned by me, but it takes a kind of reckless courage
born of faith to leave space for serendipity.*
—Arden Georgi Thompson

The Fishbowl

Twenty-four hours after the paramedics rolled me into the emergency room, I padded behind the nurse who controlled the locked door to the psych ward. A white plastic drawstring bag filled with my clothes, necklace, and dignity, all removed during a strip search, dangled at my side. Curious and scared, I investigated the sleeping ward. Through doors left ajar, I caught glimpses of ordinary hospital beds, so different from the dungeon-like accommodations I'd conjured up in my imagination.

Three small, concentric circles of light from the nurse's flashlight penetrated the darkness of a room near the center hub of the ward. The nurse spoke in a low voice so as not to wake the crazy lady in the other bed. "Your things will be in the closet. I have to lock it, so if you need something, just tell one of us. I know it feels bad, but we do it to keep you safe."

I refrained from telling her I had no plans to slip my neck through my dirty underwear.

The nurse locked the plastic laminate closet door. "There's juice and some snacks in the kitchen. It's okay to help yourself." She turned down my bed and left me to get settled.

After midnight, the nurses' station hummed with mysterious murmurs like half-heard conversations behind closed doors. Far off, a door snicked shut. With one vigilant eye on the hallway and the

117

other on the crazy lady across the room, I waited to be accosted by torturous screams, babbling, or a face with a vacant stare and loose jaw with drool rolling down its chin.

Although I'd been awake for more than forty-eight hours, I didn't want to go to sleep in that bed because it was tantamount to conceding I had no control over myself. The rubbery pillow's resistance captured the strange otherworldliness I felt; every shred of normalcy had been stripped away.

The crazy lady rose out of her bed and flicked her blankets and sheets, sending imaginary bed bugs into my space. She picked around under the covers until she found a brown lump of matted fur. I shrank back and sidled crab-wise to the far edge of my bed, fearful of having to interact with strangeness.

The woman could have used my driver's license as a fake ID. Both of us were old enough to know better than to wind up on a psych ward in February. We carried more weight than the actuarial charts advised and tucked our shoulder-length graying hair behind our ears. She toted the furry thing across the room.

"Here, don't be embarrassed. Yesterday was my first night, and I held onto him like I was two years old." She held out a cheap gift shop teddy bear. "My name is Caroline."

Only an archangel could have brought a stuffed animal to my bedside. "Thank you." I reached for it and tried to sit up at the same time. The sheets snarled with my hospital gown as I struggled to the edge of the bed. My feet worked to push the awful hospital socks off before I stuck my legs out from under the blankets—vanity first.

Inside the straight-jacket of my own making, helpless as a hobbled mule and holding onto a teddy bear, I snickered, then convulsed into unrestrained laughter, which spread like wildfire between the two of us.

The nurse pushed open the door to find two old ladies maniacally howling while pulling at mummy wrappings.

The nurse choked back laughter. "I'll get some scrubs."

Caroline sat on the edge of my bed. "How long were you in the fishbowl?"

I looked at her uncomprehendingly, unsure if I should pretend to be a fish or tell her I wasn't one. It dawned on me; the locked entrance opened into a large, glass-walled atrium: the fishbowl.

Before being taken to the ward, an intern had tried to weave screening questions into a caring dialogue. An hour later, he had closed the contrived conversation by assuring me that despite the scrutiny, the hospital respected my right to privacy, and even though confined to the unit by a hold, I could leave as soon as the doctor released me.

"Did his Adam's apple bob up and down so much you had to watch it?" Caroline moved her finger up and down from jaw to collar bone.

"Yes!"

We laid back on the bed and cackled.

The nurse returned and handed me a set of scrubs on loan from a giant. "You girls need to be quiet; there are patients who have a hard time sleeping, okay?"

I changed in the bathroom. When I came out, the nurse turned off the lights, left the door ajar, and disappeared.

Caroline peeked into the hallway to make sure the coast was clear and returned to sit on my bed. "How long have you been fucked up?"

"Just now, or long-term?"

We cackled some more and then talked about President Kennedy's assassination, how we dreamed of attending Woodstock, and how Charles Manson and Richard Speck shook our sense of invulnerability.

I told her about the archangel, and she told me about the school-bus-sized armadillo that had lumbered across the road in front of her car. We shared a jumble of memories about being harmed. Then we got to the heart of the matter and opened up about how we caused harm to others. Neither of us gave ourselves credit for doing the best we could, given the circumstances, although we saw bravery and capability in each other.

I looked at the acoustic tiled ceiling. "I don't remember what it is to be me."

Caroline responded to my comment with silence.

That night, the medication worked. For the first time since menopause began, I slept through the night.

Mornings on the ward began at seven o'clock with a call to be in the kitchen by seven-thirty. I sat near Caroline, and we chatted as if we hadn't bared our souls to one another, speaking impersonal words about inconsequential events.

A woman with fierce black hair sat across from me. "Don't you think they should put *Cinderella* on the TV? I keep telling them if everyone watched Disney, the whole world would be better." She waved her plastic fork like a magic wand, then speared the pancakes on her plate.

I tended to myself most of the morning. In the dayroom, an acrylic wall display held tired adaptations of travel brochures: *Visit the Isles of Addiction, Depression Cavern Adventures, Cruising Through Sexual Assault,* and *Behavioral Health Spas.* I straightened the pile of old magazines on a side table, then leafed through *Family Circle's* Halloween edition.

The woman with fierce black hair entered the dayroom. "Disney movies make me feel happy." She waved her invisible magic wand again. "Everyone should be happy." Bibbity, bobbity, boo.

She had a valid point, and I found myself wanting to support her. "Which is your favorite?"

"*Cinderella.*"

A nurse wearing magenta scrubs interrupted our pseudo-conversation. She invited the fairy godmother to walk with her in the hall and spoke to me over her shoulder. "Jody has schizophrenia. It's best if you let me talk to her. Why don't you go into the kitchen and make yourself a cup of tea."

I thought about the promise of confidentiality and wondered if the nurse realized she had broken it. Jody frightened me. It wasn't her disease; it was my inability to understand how to interact with her. Could my words have caused harm?

Instead of heating water, I escaped to my room. Within moments, a different nurse intruded. "Your door has to be open. You can't be in here without permission."

I don't think she meant to be unkind.

"You didn't know, so I won't enter an infraction on your chart. Check in next time, okay?"

There was no place to hide. I was a captured bug in a collecting jar. The assumption I needed supervision angered and humiliated me.

Joel visited in the late afternoon; the person in charge of the keys opened the atrium's door. We sat on a vinyl-covered institutional bench supported by shiny metallic legs made more comfortable by shiny metallic side arms.

He broke the silence. "How are you?"

He allowed my head to rest on his shoulder but didn't hug me or hold my hand, which made me feel as hopeless as when I'd walked toward the highway. Unable to look at the situation from his vantage point, I pleaded with him. "Please, Joel, take me home."

He inched away from my grasp. "I hope you find what you are looking for, Beth. You're the only one who can figure this out."

I reached for his fingers and sobbed harder.

He walked away, then turned. "Don't do it for me."

Don't do what for you? Stay alive? Die? He left again. My primal sobs didn't call him back. A nurse escorted me to my room. Her voice talked to someone; she may have thought it was me.

Within a half-hour, I met with the intern who had first assessed me. Again, he asked a battery of questions; one differed. "Do you want the nightmares to end?"

I explained insomnia to the five-year-old intellect who had graduated from medical school. "I don't sleep. That suggests I don't have very many nightmares."

That evening, I joined other patients in the queue at the nurses' station for meds. When it was my turn, the nurse flipped through her notes. "The doctor stopped your Strattera and amitriptyline. Let's see; you have..." She named meds I didn't recognize except for thorazine. The young woman slid a plastic cup toward me. "Go ahead; they'll help. You need more sleep."

Obediently, I dumped the pills into my hand, then flicked the motley collection into my mouth.

"Don't do that!"

I backed away from the counter, thinking a crazy person ran amok.

But Nurse Ratched was yelling at *me*. "Use the cup!" She handed me water which I didn't need because I had already swallowed the pills.

"Drink it anyway, then open your mouth so I can see."

I was incredulous.

The other patients who knew the routine grew restless. Once back in my room, I tucked Caroline's teddy bear under the covers of her bed, so it waited for her.

Caroline's subdued demeanor suggested something was wrong. "I'm going home tomorrow."

"Are you scared?"

"Yes."

Returning to the real world frightened us more than we cared to admit. The ward was like a nest separated from the world.

When I woke the next morning, the teddy bear waited for me at the foot of my bed. Caroline's had been stripped and waited for the next patient. The sleep meds had worked; I'd been oblivious to the sun's rise, the wake-up knock, and Caroline's departure.

During the mid-afternoon lull, the nurse escorted a stringy-haired, skeletal woman in her early twenties to the empty bed. I avoided her until nighttime. I thought the stuffed animal might comfort her as much as it had me. "Would you like to have the teddy bear?"

"Hell, no! To fuck and back, why would I want a freakin' stuffed animal?"

To fuck and back? I had never heard that particular expression. Silence settled over the ward. Later, one of the ever-changing nurses peeked in, shone her flashlight around the room, then charted her observations. I pretended to sleep, which turned out to be a mistake because the doctor thought the medication worked.

Much later, while I gazed at the space somewhere between the window glass and the parking lot, the street lamp's glow needled into long prismatic crystals. I tried to talk with the light. *How do I get home? I'm lost. I know I'm guilty, but what should I have done instead?*

The disembodied male voice returned. *Look with your heart.*

Black glowed blacker. The colored crystalline needles of light entered the room and organized into the archangel's body. He sat on my bed as if he meant to read me a story. His gray, felted feathers formed thick, scratchy wings, and their velvety tips puddled around his feet. The hospital mattress sagged under the great weight of his armor; his cruciform-hilt sword, encased in a laced, leather scabbard, stuck out straight, forcing part of his wing to fold.

The girl in the other bed gave no indication she noticed the visitation.

As before, the archangel communicated telepathically. *Light is all there is.*

Unspoken information entered my brain slowly this time. I had experienced the purity of this light when I was the universe. *Light is unbounded and infinite. Some people call this God.* He withdrew into the rainbow-hued needles of light which withdrew into the bulb. The archangel assumed his disguise, a solitary street lamp flooding the parking lot with love.

In the morning, different people joined me at the table. The angry girl who shared my room refused to eat, and Cinderella's fairy godmother paced in the hall. Cheery conversation and laughter among the others taught me that those admitted to the psych ward were ordinary people trying to put their lives back together; there were no monsters among us.

A gentle girl with delicate features who wore a tortoiseshell hair comb approached me as I placed my tray in the trolley. "You're Beth?"

"Yup."

"I'm Michelle. Your doctor wants a family history. We can work in the atrium, or I can find a different place if you prefer."

I recognized she controlled my behavior by extending a choice. I pointed to the fishbowl. "Lead on."

The sun shone through the atrium's window, painting bright rectangles on the floor. From my vantage point, the tops of the trees looked like a briar patch. My eyes gazed down on the branches because I didn't want to look at Michelle.

The disembodied male voice warned of trouble coming. *Trees of life, trees of strife.*

Michelle settled into a chair across from me. "Let's start with your parents."

"Let's not." I slid a foot across the floor to draw an imaginary line. "To fuck and back." I laughed, appreciating the new expletive, and started with my grandfather's story and my mother's secret.

"Were either diagnosed with a mental illness?"

"The newspaper article said my grandfather had bipolar disorder. Of course, he was an alcoholic. No one in the family talks much about him." I spaced out a bit, thinking about Little Birdie.

"Mom was in the hospital most of my senior year. I know she tried to commit suicide, and they gave her electroshock treatments, but no one told me the details. When dad was arrested, she was diagnosed with Munchausen syndrome. I don't know the whole story."

Michelle wrote a note in the margin of her paper. "Was she an alcoholic?"

"Only when she couldn't get Valium."

Michelle suggested we take a break. She walked toward the ward and returned with two ceramic mugs filled with steaming hot coffee. "Let's move on. Tell me about your father. You said he was arrested."

I sagged onto the sofa and rested my elbows on my knees so I could talk to the floor. "Maybe ten, fifteen years ago, I can't remember—Mom came home after having a stent put in her heart. That evening, my dad turned her chair upside down so she couldn't sit. He stomped on her bare feet with his climbing boots when she tried to leave the room. Then, he went after her with a broom and, later, he hit her with a heavy down pillow again and again during the night. Toward morning, she escaped from the house. He caught her and jammed a two-inch rock into her mouth. The neighbors called the police, and they arrested him. Now he's a felon." A grin broke out. "That finally shut him up."

"Was he an alcoholic, or did he abuse drugs?"

"Nope, he was just mean. My dad wouldn't take aspirin if it stood between him and hell."

We talked about the incident until I noticed our coffee had cooled.

"I'll get us more." I ignored her hand placed over her mug and her directive to stay. After the microwave chimed, I returned from the kitchen with two cups of stale, boiled coffee.

"Thank you. I charted the infraction of leaving our workspace. We can continue in a different room if you'd like."

I dismissed her information about the infraction because I always behaved well, which, to my mind, meant the rule didn't pertain to me. "Don't worry; I don't mind."

"Okay. I have a question you don't have to answer. Were you abused, Beth?" She leaned toward me, read my body language, and drew back.

I skated my story around as if it were a drop of mercury on waxed paper.

"My dad started making fun of me in fourth grade because I was dumb and fat. When I was thirteen, he told me he couldn't make me smart, but he had a birthday present to help with the fat part. It was a paperback book of Royal Canadian Air Force exercises, and every day until I was almost seventeen, he forced me to do them in front of him. Sometimes it aroused him, if you catch my drift."

The sensation of being watched made my skin crawl. "I stopped it by running away from home. They locked me up in a juvenile detention center, and you know what? I liked it there better than being at home."

"He did that every day?"

"Well, not on Sundays or the holidays. But, yeah, Walter Cronkite would sign off the news. I mimicked his voice. "'And that's the way it is...' Then it was my turn. My mom and sister would watch TV, and I'd perform for Dad."

My chin quivered, and I bit my lip. No matter how old I was, telling always felt as bad as when it was happening. I had become self-conscious of my body, felt its ugliness, and wanted to disappear. "One of my therapists calculated it happened over a thousand times."

Michelle held the space with me for a while before she spoke again."Was he diagnosed with a mental illness?"

"When he was in jail, they said he had schizoid personality disorder."

"Let's talk about your other relatives."

"Let's not." By sharing the parts, I communicated the whole; enough said.

If we laugh at what we do not understand, will it go away, or does laughter merely postpone meeting the unknown until another day?
—Arden Georgi Thompson

Lithium

The ward's group facilitator directed my hand toward my stomach with a butterfly's touch. She wanted me to feel the in-and-out movement of my diaphragm while learning a deep breathing technique. I shrank from her touch. Yesterday's interview had kicked memories of my father into scurrying red ants. Her touch brought him to life and stung my flaws. *Suck in that gut and lift your leg higher.* I yelped at her like a stepped-upon puppy and growled when she tried to help a second time. "Don't touch me. Don't even look!"

I bolted to my room and slammed the door. A nurse knocked. "You aren't allowed to be in your room with the door closed." Well-behaved me apologized and acknowledged another infraction. After I boycotted lunch, I followed a nurse's feet to a small office and waited for *my* doctor—the one assigned to me after the random walk that had landed me in the hospital.

Dr. Larsen wore a blazer with leather patches at the elbows, khakis, and deck shoes that were so broken in they resembled slippers. Mouse-brown hair surrounded a little boy's face. "Hello, Bethany." His steady, compassionate demeanor did nothing to dispel the anxiety provoked by the use of my Christian name. It raised more red ant memories of my father. *Bethany Lynne, you'd gag a maggot.*

The doctor leaned back in his chair and placed one foot on his knee. "Do you remember answering questions yesterday?"

I nodded.

"I have some rating scales I'd like you to complete. Some of the questions will be the same; some will be different. Is that something you can do?"

I accepted the challenge and flew through the items on the checklists.

Had I ever felt the opposite of depression? Had I come across any brilliant ideas? I considered my trip to Barnes & Noble. Indeed, I had been euphoric, the opposite of depressed. My idea of writing a book with my students had seemed genuinely brilliant. Secretly, I had been sure Cornell would accept it as a Ph.D. dissertation.

Did I have trouble sleeping? Had my mood affected my relationships? Well, I had filled many spiral notebooks, writing until night kissed dawn, and I'd walked away from my marriage. Did that count?

Did I have any experience with telepathy? Did things appear differently than usual? Would the angel be angry if I told of his visitations? Could the doctor understand the mystical revelations of Einstein's equation? What about the disembodied voice, the pigeon feathers that had turned into otherworldly art, or the rapture of Barnes & Noble?

How much of that could I disclose without sounding crazy?

I handed the few papers to Dr. Larsen. He reviewed them, then set them aside and asked an unexpected question. "Is anyone you know suffering?"

This question halted my thinking. I wondered. The word was one I reserved for victims of the Holocaust or for Christ nailed to the cross. Yet, I knew Joel suffered. The idea fit. I didn't think about myself.

He shifted his attention to my chart. "You seem irritable."

The inaccuracy broke my silence. "I'm not irritable. I am ir-ri-ta-ted." To me, the comment summed up the situation succinctly.

Dr. Larsen remained quiet while he considered our dialogue and flipped through his notes. After an exaggerated pause, the doctor delivered horrible news. "Bethany, I believe you have bipolar disorder."

You motherfucker! Was I about to get locked away like my grandfather? Were they going to shoot electricity through my head as they did my mother? *SHIT!* I imagined Joel running like hell away from me. My dad was right—I was more trouble than I was worth.

Dr. Larsen interrupted. "What are you thinking?"

I looked him in the eye and thought about telling him he was a prick but stayed polite. "Nothing good."

Dr. Larsen had more to say, but I only caught one word—lithium.

Hearing that startled me more than being told I had bipolar disorder. "I know someone who took lithium. I watched her change from a ballet dancer into the Michelin Man. For God's sake, her mother wiped the drool from her mouth. I'm not taking it!"

"Lithium is the gold standard for treating bipolar disorder, Bethany. What you saw was lithium toxicity. I won't let that happen to you." He told me about side effects, one of which was the possibility of gaining weight.

The reason I refused to take it was simple: I didn't want to get fat. Despite Dr. Larsen's assurance, I saw myself becoming a corpulent, drooling old lady who sat staring into space with vacant eyes. That was a state worse than being flattened by a truck.

Running the gauntlet of finding an alternative began. Dr. Larsen checked on me the next day; I sat on the small metal chair sandwiched between the desk and the wall. "How are you doing?"

"I'm fine." Defeated, I tipped my head against the wall. "I want to go home."

"If you were fine, you wouldn't be here."

I wanted to spit at the little truth-teller, but that wouldn't have been lady-like.

He transferred me from the hospital into the psychiatric day treatment unit called Partial. I'd be home for dinner, sleep in my bed at night, and participate in the hospital's program by day. During the ensuing three weeks, Dr. Larsen and I tried five different medications. The side effects were intolerable. No one can live well locked inside a bathroom. It was the tremors, though, that scared me the most.

Toward the end of my time at Partial, Dr. Larsen confronted me. "You aren't tolerating any of the meds we've tried. I'm afraid you're going to have a relapse. This is serious; I want you on lithium."

"No, I won't take it; it's for crazy people."

"Bethany, do you realize bipolar disorder is a life-threatening illness?"

We were at loggerheads. I never completed my suicide attempt; therefore, I believed my life wasn't very threatened. I discounted the data that suggested those with bipolar disorder were twenty times more likely to commit suicide than the general population.[3]

"I'll try Depakote with you. If that doesn't work and you will not take lithium, I will no longer see you as a patient." He rolled his chair to his desk and snapped at his keyboard. He leaned toward the screen and muttered to himself. "Nothing worse than a manic old lady."

My snort almost erupted into giggles that might have escalated to make me pee my pants. I stretched my neck, sat on my hands, and bit my lip to silence it. I thought about letting him know I'd overheard him, but the moment was endearing, and I didn't want to cause him embarrassment. In the past, I had voiced my frustration with unkind remarks about many students in my career; it meant I connected deeply enough to be bothered by their behavior.

I tolerated Depakote for three days, and Dr. Larsen expressed hope, but on the fourth day, I puked on the side of the road while driving to the outpatient program. I called in, as required, and returned home. Once Depakote left my system, I felt better.

Lithium is the third element in the periodic table, the only combination of protons not original to the universe or organized within a star's core or during a supernova. In 1949, lithium was discovered to be effective in controlling bipolar disorder. The U.S.

3. Baldessarini, Ross J., Maurizio Pompili, Leonardo Tondo. "Suicide in bipolar disorder: Risks and management," *CNS Spectr* (June 2006): 11(6): 465–471. doi: 10.1017/s1092852900014681

Food and Drug Administration approved it in 1970, the year I entered high school. I swallowed my first tablet at 2:40 p.m. on March 14th of the year 2012.

Being in the hospital's protective milieu had been a hiatus of sorts, and leaving the day treatment program meant I had to return to life. The most pressing issue was my job. It was late March, so going back to the classroom after April vacation made sense.

I trusted Torey, the assistant superintendent, to help me sort through my choices.

Torey fiddled with a pencil. "Do you feel well enough to come back?"

I did not, and both of us agreed to extend my sick leave.

"What about Lucy? I need to finish what I started. Someone's going to convince her she can't do math again because they can't work by doubling."

"Beth, all of your students will adjust. Mr. Blanchard met with your class when school started in January. Their new teacher took over. It's okay to let them go."

My silent reflection denied it.

Torey continued. "Look, every day students have to deal with the loss of a teacher. Remember when Ruth had cancer or when Doug died? We gave kids the best support possible. We did the same for you."

Hearing her words both confronted and comforted me. I learned no one was as important as they think they are, and I understood I didn't hold the rest of Lucy's life in my hands. She and I would remember some of our time together and forget most.

Torey's reminder followed me out the door. "Oh, and I need a doctor's note so I can rehire your sub for a long-term position."

⁂

One year after vacuuming the sidewalk, and four months after Christmas, I realized I didn't want to live in my apartment anymore. The goats were gone, and so was Joel. This time, bipolar disorder didn't curl its finger and whisper sweet nothings about adventure in my ear. It was time to move on.

Ingrid helped again. She had an empty apartment in her home that needed a tenant. It was as if the universe provided my new address. I moved to a neighboring town.

On the last day at my old apartment, I wore one of Joel's cast-off flannel plaid shirts. Plants, cleaning supplies, and the last dribs and drabs that had escaped packing boxes filled my car. Spring was in the air.

I pulled out of the driveway and followed the road down the hill one last time. I stopped to carry on an imagined conversation with the streetlight. *I'm not the same.*

No, you aren't, and you shouldn't be. A lot has happened.

Will it ever be okay?

The street light shined even though it was daytime. *You will always be different, but I trust you'll find the way.*

A car pulled up behind me, forcing me to end the conversation. I entered the highway, letting go of the home I had shared with Joel.

At Ingrid's, I unpacked boxes late into the night. Allison had hidden a present in a box filled with pots and pans. The next day, I untied the baker's twine.

Ingrid read her card to me. *I know you don't feel at home. I'm down the road. Come visit any time.* The gift was a jigsaw puzzle of delicate porcelain teacups.

I wrestled my small dining room table up the stairs and set it under the window so I could look through the branches of the linden tree into Ingrid's garden. I sorted through the pieces of my puzzle, thinking about the ones inside my brain.

When I spilled the contents of the box onto the table, some pieces fell to the floor. I bent down to pick them up, and my knee shook. I reached again, and the tremor returned. I experimented. Raising my heel to put weight on the ball of my foot started the quiver; lowering my heel made it stop. Odd.

Days passed. One evening I reached for my mug. My thumb didn't have enough strength to steady it, and tea spilled. Occasionally, I needed to wipe the drool from the corner of my mouth.

I called Dr. Larsen's office. "I need to make an appointment, please."

"Let's see. I have an opening on July 23rd. What's your name?"

Three months away? I needed him now! I hung up and drove to the day treatment program. Within an hour, I sat across from Dr. Larsen.

"Bethany, how are you today?"

I wanted to avoid inspection. I felt disrobed and too ugly to be on display because I believed the failure was mine. I told Dr. Larsen about the shaking, the weakness in my thumb, and the damned drool.

Dr. Larsen turned his back to me, tapped on his keyboard, and evaluated the situation—and me. "Let's cut back on lithium. I want bloodwork done, and I want you to check in with the outpatient RN once a week. I won't admit you into the program; just stop by. Yes?"

I wanted to tell Dr. Larsen I had just fallen in trust with him. He was true to his word. I had a partner who would help me manage an illness I would have for the rest of my life. He wasn't an authoritarian enemy whose mission was to override my autonomy. I let go of my doubts and embraced our alliance.

I didn't mention other oddities. At times, my vocal cords sounded as if a novice drew a violin bow across them. Multisyllabic words no longer rolled off my tongue. The television irritated me.

The fact I couldn't read[4] escaped me. Junk mail looked junky, store names didn't need decoding, and brownie mix came with visual instructions. I didn't need letters, words, or paragraphs to function in my daily life. That I had needed Ingrid's help to read Allison's note didn't help me connect the dots.

---

4. Acquired dyslexia was caused by permanent damage to the visual cortex of my brain. My language deficit was due to stress and resolved over time. My ability to write was never compromised.

One day, I opened the microwave to heat water for tea, only to find two steaming mugs waiting. Another day, I held a pan in one hand and a box of macaroni and cheese in the other, but couldn't figure out their connection, only that they were edges of something I needed to bring together.

One evening, Ingrid poked her head into my apartment. "Dinner's getting cold; you told me you'd be over."

"I did? I'll be right there."

Later, Ingrid knocked. "I went ahead and made a plate for you. Here's a loaf of fresh bread too."

It never occurred to me I owed her an apology for standing her up until the day we laughed about it while drinking tea under the linden tree.

Bills arrived, but I couldn't make heads or tails of what was what. I took my checkbook to Ingrid. "These people printed their bills wrong. Look at them! How is a person supposed to figure them out?"

"Let's look."

She read the amount to pay, and I wrote checks. My beautiful penmanship looked like a first grader's.

During the long months I was on sick leave, the biting mania and smothering depression loosened their grip. A vacuum replaced the intensity of unrelenting extremes. I made up lesson plans to pass the time in which nothing happened. Day in and day out, I got up in the morning, opened cans of food, and sat in a chair.

I started journaling again, during the morning, while the rest of the world went to work or to school.

Joel reached out. He stopped by and helped with little tasks. He replaced a blown light bulb, brought a plant to sit on my puzzle table, and delivered Chinese food.

As wonderful as it was to see him, I knew saying goodbye was part of his hello.

Distant mountains seem so very high until we stand upon
the final peak at last and realize that now the ground upon
which we stand is flat. Height, difficulty, and distance
all seem relative to where the observing I is at.
—Arden Georgi Thompson

Bug Splat

My substitute's name had replaced mine on the spreadsheet that listed all the district's positions. She'd be starting school at Jefferson Elementary come September, not me. The superintendent didn't bother to hide the master list from me. In fact, it seemed to be arranged on his desk to save him from having to tell me I'd been replaced.

We spoke of this and that, then Mark, endearingly soft-spoken, cleared his throat before speaking. "Beth, if you come back, I have to put you in seventh grade at the middle school." He scowled, and I felt ashamed to be the cause of his frustration.

The words *if you come back* stung like a hornet. Leaving my teaching position wasn't an option for me because the state had denied my application for disability twice, and there weren't many career opportunities for a fifty-six-year-old woman. Most worrisome, if I didn't work three more semesters, I wouldn't qualify for early retirement and would lose my pension altogether.

Being put in seventh grade, though, was as good as saying he'd plunk me back home with the people, the place, and things I had left behind when bipolar disorder's fickle thinking dared my brain to move to fourth grade. I could return to *my* school, where the herd stampeded like rhinoceroses or glided by like gazelles, followed by the meek and mild. Students would arrive in September already proficient at boarding yellow buses and balancing cafeteria trays. On the first day, the only skill to master would be opening combination locks.

I didn't know how to broach the elephant in the room. I secretly cheered because the change meant I no longer needed to explain my failure to Mr. Blanchard or face Mrs. Westcott's judgment.

Mark pulled the list of teaching positions available in the district toward him and flipped to the middle school section. "We had to change things due to enrollment increases." He shifted in his chair. "You'll have to teach social studies second semester."

I avoided discussing politics or religion with others, preferring less controversial topics such as microbial ecology, Newton's laws, or thinking. Give me a linear equation, not a debate. My superintendent knew me well enough to recognize the enormity of the challenge.

He penciled my name into the master list under *Grade Seven, Split Position*, then looked up at me. "I need a doctor's note to allow you back in the classroom."

Outside Central Office, I leaned against the brick wall and closed my eyes with relief while fearful thoughts about the upcoming school year swarmed like flies over raw meat. I resolved to take the next action—and not think too far ahead. The only choice was to force the pieces to fall into place before September.

I was no expert in social studies, but I knew how a textbook worked. On my way home, I swung by the middle school and borrowed a teachers' edition. I thought if I could just get to know the new curriculum, there might be a chance to get through until June.

Once home, I set the manual on my puzzle table, opened the book to the first chapter, and read the introductory sentence without success. I tried again, then went downstairs to make tea. I put clothes in the dryer, checked the mail, and swept the porch. Returning upstairs, I flipped through the book, craving a cup of tea.

I recognized the shape of the table of contents; chapters used color codes and recognizable structural elements. But the words may as well have been Egyptian hieroglyphics. Only one black shape would translate into English at a time; it was as if I scanned the print with a clear marble to bring each letter into focus, then chained the letters together to solve the puzzle of finding a word.

I moved the book to the bottom of my to-do pile since I wouldn't need to begin social studies until after Christmas break. Meanwhile, I could teach science in the dark to zombies; it was the paperwork that was problematic. I didn't care about red tape, anyway, so I ignored it.

I made an appointment with Dr. Grant.

She knocked on the examining room's door before entering. "Hi, Bethany, how's it going?"

"I'm getting ready to go back to school."

"Are you excited or worried?"

"Both, hanging on by the skin of my teeth, actually. I need another note to go back to work."

"Are you sure you're up to it?"

"I have to be."

Without asking about the details, Dr. Grant wrote a note, then ripped it from her pad's rubbery spine. "Let me know if you have any problems."

I didn't think to mention my inability to read.

The battle to recover my reading skills began in the grocery store. Once a week, Joel came to the rescue and took me shopping at the store with the green and orange sign. Past the automatic doors, a cacophony of sounds invaded my brain: the whoosh of the doors, the deli's bell, cranky children, and squeaky carts; all vied for attention.

The store stank, a continuous gradient of cake blended with cheese, merging with fish. Mothers with children jostled past me. As Joel chose items, I located simple words on the packaging: egg, bread, sugar, soup. Soon, I recognized more complex ones: cauliflower, bologna, and mozzarella.

Joel didn't understand how difficult it was to figure out what I wanted to eat. "You can't keep buying seven cans of ravioli every week. Let's get some chicken; you pick two kinds of fresh vegetables. I'll stay and make sure you don't burn the house down while you cook."

I stood behind him as we checked out, surreptitiously pulling gossip magazines from the rack. On the covers of *People*, *Us*, and the *National Enquirer*, I found names with pictures: K for Kate, *Kate Middleton*, and J for Jennifer, *Jennifer Aniston*.

⁂

August's humid, hot weather signaled it was time to shuttle my school belongings from above Ingrid's garage back to the middle school. Allison passed a box to Sean.

"Moving your stuff is getting old, Mom."

Who made the comment? I didn't know.

The old building, once a high school, boasted six science laboratories. In mine, the black soapstone countertop of a grand old oak demonstration bench defined the focal point. Twelve tables filled the center area.

I claimed my half of a shared prep room by washing the glassware and reorganizing materials. Arranged on the shelves, my personal stash of cornstarch, baking soda, plastic cups, and plates, Coke, Mentos, vinegar, LEGOs, and glue barely fit into the spacious storage area. I'd reserved an empty student locker to store a blow-up kiddie pool, cookie sheets, and a bowling ball.

Vintage *Dick and Jane* books, tied with wide red ribbon and angled just so beside the lamp, disguised the primers as decorative items. Secretly, as often as possible, I read the simple stories using an index card, sliding my finger along to isolate words. When finished, I slipped the books back inside the ribbon.

The teacher who had fostered my cockroaches returned them.

On the morning of the first day, my favorite globes of the gray moon, rusted Mars, Venus, and Earth hung from the ceiling. Cobalt curtains accented the warm earth tones of oak wall display cases and cream-colored walls. Placemats and table runners of emerald green set off fossils and defined my microscope station. Shelving held my library of beautiful, organized books.

Confident and secure in my stained-glass chamber of math and science, I ventured into the hall to watch the buses arrive. A young girl darted through the front door and frantically searched the hall. "The nurse! I need the nurse!"

What that child needed was a sink. Her sister had thrown up on the bus and used her gargantuan purse as a basin. The seventh-grader's panic stemmed from the danger posed to the mascara she carried with her.

I led the way to my prep room, where we washed myriad boxes of blush and eye shadow and one precious lone vial of mascara. We chatted; Sammie revealed she was new to the school.

"I understand that feeling!" I told her about the Jefferson School while she worried about whether or not her purse would stink. "Let's see what it's like at the end of the day. Do you want to keep your stuff here so it can air out?"

She didn't—everything went back into her wet faux leather purse. The bell rang. Sammie went her way, and I went mine.

For my first lesson, I split my seventh-graders into teams. I noticed an outlier, one of those kiddos who hated school. "No groups smaller than one."

He gave me the stink eye. "You can't have a group smaller than one."

"I don't know; sometimes, people don't want to work with themselves." I walked away to let him solve the problem. During that lull, when individuals synchronized, I handed an envelope and a large sheet of bulletin board paper to each team. Their eyes rolled when they read my essential question: *How does the universe work?*

One lone voice expressed his woe. "But I don't know. You didn't tell me."

I offered reassurance. "Don't worry; you've experienced enough of the universe to figure it out." His facial expression informed me I was daft. I appealed to that unique sense of seventh grade superiority. "Seriously, I've known eighth graders who figured it out; you'll be fine."

After school, I went to the grocery store and bought five gallons of milk and lots of food coloring. I created index cards with perspective prompts. *Pretend you are a forest. Pretend you are a telescope. Pretend you are a rock cliff, a cyclotron, the sun, a microscope.*

"What's a cyclotron?" The child who received that card didn't have a question; he demanded an explanation.

"The website's URL is on your card."

I passed out plastic plates. A few students wore them as hats. I poured milk until it covered the bottom of each dish, by-passing those who wore haute couture.

Putting food coloring into the hands of seventh-graders required caution. I demonstrated how to gently deposit a small amount under the surface of the milk. One by one, squeezable vials of blue, red, green, and yellow dye moved from my control into my students'. Mesmerized by making puddles of color, no one thought about squirt guns.

Applying a touch of dish soap on the milk's surface caused color to erupt and move in wondrous swirling patterns. Very exciting! Chattering like little children, they watched. Inevitably they stirred the milk with their fingers or pencils to make it go faster.

Their messes couldn't be unstirred, so I carefully slid twenty plastic plates filled with brown milk into a basin and set it aside. I passed out twenty new set-ups, poured more milk, and we started over. "Be on the lookout for pieces getting pushed or pulled."

"Milk doesn't have pieces."

"Read the nutritional label." I handed him a milk container while addressing the rest of the class. "This time, read your index card and let your thinking watch too."

"I have to be a cyclotron?"

"Only in your imagination."

By the end of the day, I had poured five gallons of milk and washed 300 plastic plates. I blissfully danced on the knife's edge of directing inquiring minds, honed by watching the relationship between understanding and cluelessness in my students' minds.

By the end of the week, students thought about the universe as a collection of objects pushed and pulled through time. Hubble's images revealed galaxies at a large scale, and cyclotrons revealed the guts of atoms from the perspective of the very tiny. Helping students think about the parts of systems, the pushes and pulls that organized them, and how those relationships changed through time drove my curriculum: Dr. Derek Cabrera's thinking skills in action.

Some student names stuck. Aaron, a burly combative student, walked with a slow cadence that broadcasted defiance without saying a word. Kyle knew enough about anyone or anything to make his peers feel small but couldn't pass a test. The queen bee, Skye, and her minions were unforgettable. I knew each of my other students well but couldn't attach a name to their faces.

I collected papers from a hundred students every day, either homework assignments, worksheets, quizzes, or writing prompts. Red tape and learning got snarled. My pile of ungraded papers grew into a breathing, slithering pile of scales. Parents began asking questions.

When the pile reached a critical height, I lifted the whole wad and added it to a stack near my desk. Inch by inch, the stack rose like a hooded cobra emerging from a snake charmer's basket.

In the teacher's room, I lost classroom sets of worksheets, thinking the warm papers in my hands belonged to someone else, not remembering I had just removed them from the photocopier. I copied more to fix the problem. Twice, I welcomed a teacher on my team to the school, thinking she was a new hire. Sometimes, I wandered around on the second floor, trying to find my classroom located one level down. By the time the semester drew to an end, too many loose ends and fumbled balls caught up with me.

Jen, the special education teacher who popped in and out of my classroom on a daily basis to help students, had observed my difficulties all semester. She spent more time than usual outside my door talking with Anna, the literacy coach. One of them always rescued me when I forgot I needed to be in the cafeteria or at a meeting. Sometimes, we chatted about how frustrating teaching had become for me. I never shared that I couldn't read, although Jen might have known because she'd become adept at finding lost papers that sat two inches from my hand.

A week away, Christmas break ensured epic battles would pit students who looked forward to new iPhones against those who hoped to eat on each vacation day. I was depleted and had to behave as if I were not.

The eleven-thirty recess bell launched bodies like a catapult. Swept up by my problems, I only wanted to get through the day. Recess duty was an unwelcome challenge. The fight du jour would need a ref, and I was on call.

Sammie sat at the back table of my classroom with her head draped across her arm. It was her come-hither-but-stay-far-away pose. I approached her table and pulled up a chair. "Come on, sweetie, I have recess duty." I flicked my shoes into the corner and pulled on my furry boots.

This beautiful child believed she wore an ugly skin. Her long dark hair needed shampooing but still managed to curl down her back. "Can't I stay here? I promise I'll read my book."

"I know you would, but I can't say yes; you know that. Come on." I tapped my finger on the table. "I know you're brave enough."

The gist of her response was a no-thank-you.

"Come on, it isn't the worst day; no one puked in your purse. Let's go." Usually, that comment would draw a giggle, breaking the grip of her dark musings, allowing her foul mood to bead onto her skin, then puddle to the floor.

Sammie lifted her head and heaved a sigh as only she could. She shouldered her purse while I collected my mittens. I considered grabbing a couple of hand warmers from my bottom drawer to ward off the winter chill but didn't have the energy. Following Sammie, I turned off the lights, then closed and locked the old wooden door behind me.

My dream of being a teacher had begun in fourth grade, but on this day, I just wanted to hang on for three more semesters until I could retire. I knew I was too ill to finish the school year, but that didn't stop me from continuing the masquerade—there was no alternative.

Outside, the knee-deep snow was beautiful except for the dirty piles left by the plow. The playground, nothing more than a section of the parking lot set off by orange cones, was iced with bodies in motion. My soon-to-be migraine pulsed with the metallic ring of frozen basketballs pounding against the school's only backboard. I positioned myself behind the fray.

Beyond the melee of the basketball game, a knot of girls pressed against the side of the school's storage shed, quiet and still.

Something was very wrong.

It was Sammie. Her unprotected forehead leaned against the cold wall; tension tugged her emotional kite string toward its breaking point. Her few friends flocked around her, trying to keep her grounded. A larger body of students watched, perhaps hoping they would get to see her string snap.

Fear rocked my heart. "Sammie, it's me, Mrs. Davis. Do you know I'm here?"

Her hand reached for mine. I took it.

Mr. Foyett moved to the edge of the basketball game. He held up the walkie-talkie, and I acknowledged the need to call for administrative support. Then, I turned my attention to the crowd.

"Sammie needs some privacy. You're really good friends, but let me help her now."

They would have no part of it. They mirrored me and reached to touch her; one latched onto her hand and another fingered Sammie's hair.

Rebekah's matter-of-fact voice growled. "She has rat poison in her purse."

Gabbie repeated Rebekah's words in a whisper. "She has rat poison, Mrs. Davis."

We locked eyes. "I heard you, lovey; it's in her purse. I'll take care of it. Let's give her some space."

Watching Sammie shook my bones because I recognized myself. In seventh grade, I, too, had staged such a threat. I didn't carry rat poison; instead, I chose salt tablets from the back of the medicine chest; my mother had bought them before we drove through the desert southwest to stave off dehydration. They were big and white and looked lethal.

Sammie wasn't a worry in the short term. The school's guidance counselor was caring and capable. The nurse would take the rat poison. The principal would summon her mother, who would come and express her love by scolding her daughter.

I had similarly shared my suicidal ideations in the past. It wasn't until that moment that I realized I had caused distress in others. No one had been able to alleviate my pain, but they would have given anything to be able to do so. I had hoped they'd hand me an aspirin to alleviate my psychological pain or perhaps call 911.

But no one in my audience was a psychic surgeon; no one could reach in and cut out what hurt. Those who would have given me the shirt off their back couldn't clothe my naked spirit. I probably triggered painful thoughts of suicide in some who tried to help me.

Sammie's pain wasn't relieved that day. Her drama revealed the magnitude of her distress. I looked into the eyes of Mrs. Marks, the guidance counselor, as I transferred Sammie's hand to hers. Where was help for these children? Would life be as hard for her as it was for me?

*We're not made of gold; we're part of all the elements
of Earth. Please open yourselves to accept our gifts;
without your open hearts and hands, we have no worth.*
—Arden Georgi Thompson

Unmasked

The bell rang, marking the end of recess. Sammie had been inside for twenty minutes.

Mrs. Marks waited while I stomped the snow from my boots and removed my mittens after entering the building, a vast bubble of warm air filled with noise. "Your scarf's dragging." She pulled it up and straightened it. "Sammie's mom is already here. She'd like to talk."

A tall woman with the same long, dark hair as her daughter waited in the office. Sunken eyes framed by purple circles contrasted with her pale skin, and her gaunt, skeletal face glowed with joy as she approached me with outstretched hands. "Thank you for caring about my daughter."

"Of course!" I basked in Sammie's mother's goodwill and wondered where she found the strength to exude such an affirmation of life. I'd glimpsed this same personality trait hidden under Sammie's depression.

Her mom released my hand and rocked her heavy purse behind her hip. "She wants to talk with you before we leave."

Sammie sat at Mrs. Marks' table, fiddling with the guidance counselor's collection of troll dolls. "Today's my last day. I wasn't going to tell anyone." Sammie heaved her purse onto the table. "I really like you, so I asked my mom if I could say goodbye."

145

"Oh, sweet girl, I'm so glad you did."

"My mom has cancer. I've been trying to cook and keep the house up, but it's too hard. We're moving, so my aunt will be close enough to help. That's where I'll be for Christmas." Sammie's face rippled into a teasing grin. "I thought I might do my homework at my new school, just for you."

Her revelation startled me. Usually, the school knew more about a student's circumstances. I hid my surprise by thumping my hand against my sternum. "Sammie's going to do her schoolwork?" I did a pratfall onto the floor. "Oh, my God, call 911!"

Our laughter vented stress.

Sammie stood and shouldered her purse. "Bye, Mrs. Davis."

She gave me a lingering hug, and I whispered into her unkempt hair, disguising my sadness. "Goodbye, dearest child."

We parted. Sammie left with her mother, disappearing the way students do, another Cheshire cat inside my heart. An observer probably wouldn't have noticed.

Instead of grabbing coffee during the last five minutes of my twenty-minute lunch break, I filled out the incident report the school nurse had placed in my mailbox. The document required a description of the incident's cause. Sadness? Fear? Uncertainty? Love?

Three door knobs away, my classroom promised to rescue me from impending doom. My car key wouldn't open the door, no matter which way I turned it. I let my wet coat and scarf fall to the floor while I studied my key fob, aware Anna watched from her office across the empty hall. Defeated, I asked for help. "Can you open the door for me?"

She flicked through my keys until she found the right one, then stepped around my coat and wet scarf to open the door.

I stared at the floor, ashamed such a simple task had proven too complicated.

"I'm tired of failing, and now I can't even open a fucking door!" I slid down the wall, broken and subdued, and sat on the cold floor tiles. My arms hugged my knees, and my head slumped to rest upon them. Hoping Anna would hear, I spoke to the air. "I'm hospital bait."

Anna bent down and pulled me to my feet. She offered to teach my class so I could take a break, but, unable to conjure up a lesson plan, not even the one I'd repeated three times that morning, I refused her generosity. Perhaps I knew the next section of students would be the last of my career.

Instead of collapsing, I reached into my bag of tricks. It was time to trust my teaching and play with my students one last time. It was going to be a Coke and Mentos[5] afternoon. I pulled the kiddie pool out of my locker. Then, I cut open a large black trash bag, climbed up on a table, and tucked its edges into the dropped ceiling grid.

When Jared entered the room, I asked him to inflate the kiddie pool, thus ensuring the most challenging student would be very busy. The rest of the students and I shuttled the lab tables and chairs to the wall's edge.

The kids took over. They knew it was a Coke and Mentos afternoon. "What's the variable?"

I removed the bottom drawer from my bench and dumped my entire collection of chemical hand warmers on the slate counter. "Heat."

Notebooks whipped out of backpacks. Like magic, every student found a pencil. Heads together and butts up, my students argued about how to test the effect, if any, heat had on a Coke and Mentos system.

One student asked the question I hadn't thought all the way through. "How many of those can we use?"

I shouldn't have emptied my drawer, as I had quite a few. "I'll give away a dozen."

"Do we have to have a control?"

I answered with a raised eyebrow and calculated how long I should let those bottles bake.

---

5. When combined, Diet Coke and Mentos release carbon dioxide gas, producing a geyser effect.

Adding Mentos to the first bottle of Coke, the control at room temperature, caused it to bubble over the top, leaving a small amount of sticky foam on the bottom of the wading pool—no surprise. I watched in astonishment as the eruption from the second bottle, wrapped in two hand warmers, topped out two feet shy of the ceiling.

I shared my students' palpable joy as we awaited the eruption from the third bottle, which was wrapped in four hand warmers. I studied the black plastic bag and tallied the cost of replacing ceiling tiles.

We uncapped the bottle, pushed in the Mentos, and stood back to watch in awe. The spout raised, lifted, and then lifted yet again. Its surface touched the plastic on the ceiling; so far, so good.

Brown sticky foam spread out into a mushroom cloud. Inch by inch, it reached toward the edge of the black plastic. *Shit!* The geyser was gaining ground. The foamy syrup touched the far edge of the plastic and fell in fat droplets to the floor.

I plucked the fourth bottle, wrapped in six hand warmers, from its position at the side of the wading pool and smiled at the children. "I can't wait to see what happens with this one on field day!"

Amid the groans, one voice put his agony into words. "Mrs. Davis, you can't do this to me!"

The bell saved me; for a seventh grader, the only thing better than opening that Coke bottle was the end of class before Christmas break.

The last hour of the day was my planning period. I mopped away the evidence of our grand and glorious experiment while munching leftover Mentos. I avoided reality for as long as I could, then turned the lights off and closed my door. The arduous task of complicating things continued.

Intent upon isolating the papers I needed to grade for report cards, I reached for the top of the stack of papers near my desk—the cobra. It spilled forward. My mind turned the motion into a real snake, and I snapped away from the serpent's fangs, causing most of the paper scales to slither across the floor.

I curled up under my desk and cried, my eyes red and face pale.

Jen knocked on my door, let herself in, took in the scene, and left. She returned with a weighted vest designed for students with autism.

My colleague reached under my desk and arranged it around my shoulders, a gesture more comforting than words. She seemed to know I needed time to recover, not an opportunity to talk. After a reassuring squeeze on my knee, Jen left me alone in the darkened room.

The migraine that lurked during recess exploded into my eye, and tension fishhooked my jaw to my ear. After a while, the vest's soothing heaviness calmed me.

Giving up, I scooped up the papers and carried the cobra—ungraded final exams, homework, projects, unused worksheets, and all the other flotsam and jetsam accumulated over the course of the semester—to the dumpster, one armload at a time.

The metal door squealed open, and I addressed its stinking emptiness as if it were a comrade in arms. "How appropriate. We have both lost our shit." My laugh echoed.

⁂

While my students enjoyed the first day of Christmas vacation, the staff returned to school the following morning to a full agenda. A notice directed us to the high school to attend a mandatory workshop. The topic? Suicide.

A recent cluster of students, one of whom was Devon, had taken their own lives. We needed to process our losses as a staff. An expert would introduce methods for recognizing and handling students with suicidal ideations. In the auditorium, I sat alone in a crowd considering how to end my life.

I don't know what I expected—perhaps a huge circle where we would make sympathy cards for one another—like exchanging Valentines. Instead, stinging anger and divisive responses rang out. One faction wanted a bench placed in the garden. The other camp worried it might inspire copycat behavior.

A teacher stood and raged. "We've lost kids in car accidents. Why the hell didn't you want to put in a bench for them?"

Acrimonious voices spat back and forth throughout the auditorium. I felt as though the whole staff was angry with me because I hovered on the brink of suicide, although apart from Jen and Anna, no one knew how fragile I was.

Only my skin made it back to school two hours later. My brain was as fragile as a mercury glass Christmas ornament. For me, it was midnight at the masquerade ball, and my disguise was about to be ripped off. Nothing could set things right. The only way to avoid the unmasking was to be dead.

Friday at 5:30 a.m., I awoke to my alarm clock's buzz in an unfamiliar dark room. I thought the clock was broken, so I unplugged it. The window had moved to a different wall. Had I rearranged the furniture in the night? It took time to remember I was safe within my new apartment at Ingrid's house.

I turned beneath the blankets and clutched Joel's shirt to comfort my hurting heart. It had lost its scent long ago. *Joel, please, take me home.* Outside the window, snow fell like flour sifted from the clouds.

Fumbling my way to the bathroom, I decided it had to be the middle of the night. But the clock—the alarm had gone off—so I changed my mind. It had to be morning. But the streetlights were on. Was it night after all?

Confusion veiled the space between my hand and my thinking. In the dark, tired and bewildered, I made a mistake and one dose of Ambien, a hypnotic sedative, slid down my throat.

I lingered in the shower. Shimmering reality washed warmth down my body. A bolt of awareness suggested I may have been underwater for too long and was late for work.

I still had shampoo in my hair when I wrapped a soft towel around my headache.

The morning seemed different; it was dark enough to be night. My brain couldn't think for itself, and the Ambien was kicking in.

The clock, lying lifeless on the nightstand, couldn't tell me the time. I dressed, found my school bag filled with a ream of more disorganized student work, and shrugged on a coat. The towel got in the way of my hat.

I looked out of my kitchen window and saw Ingrid enjoying peanut-butter toast in her part of the house. Through her kitchen window, I watched as she lifted her mug of coffee as a cheerful greeting. It didn't seem odd I was late for work while she, who taught just down the hall, was still eating breakfast.

Why wasn't my coffee maker working? It laughed at me. *You didn't plug me in; it's time for bed.* Having no coffee made me angry because it seemed as if it would be a four- or five-cup day.

Breathing the cold December air did nothing to jolt my half awake mind. If I'd known I was impaired, of course, I would have called in sick, not started the car. I had no reason to think anything was amiss except, well, just the strangeness.

The deep rumble of my Challenger's Hemi engine growled at the snow. Ingrid told me later I backed out onto the sidewalk across the street. The fine-grained snow may as well have been a blinding blizzard. Inside a car with smooth wide racing tires, I negotiated the route toward school at five miles per hour.

A slight right-hand veer in the road led to a gentle downhill slope that terminated at a stop sign. At first, I believed I could recover from the sinuous fishtail; however, no cars were in my way, so it seemed prudent to avoid trouble by veering off the road into deep snow.

My car door became a plow to move aside the drift so I could get out. A red truck stopped, and a voice skipped across my car's roof. "Are you okay?"

"I'm fine." I jerked my bag out of the car, spilling the forgotten papers into the gentle wind that played with them. My high heels were perfect ice picks.

The disembodied voice, the one that had spoken to me in the gift shop when I bought the mice, issued a command. "*Get the papers.*"

I post-holed through the snow to gather them.

Hellbent on walking to school, I thrust the key to my thirty-thousand-dollar car into the red truck's driver's hand without looking at his face. "Brent's Garage is over there; just give them these and tell them to tow my car out of the snow. They'll know what to do."

The rest was a flicker of snippets. I refused his offer of a ride; he took my keys to the nearby auto repair shop several hundred yards away. I followed him, floundering through the snow in heels with wet, soapy hair.

When I arrived at the garage, the men were trying to figure out what to do with the distraught woman and orange Dodge Challenger that sat askew, buried in snow, on the side of the road. I gave the head mechanic my credit card, who tried to give it back.

"No, you keep it. I'll need it." Even I knew that made no sense. Then, I stormed out of the garage, still intent on hiking to school, but made it no further than the edge of the road.

Someone insisted I get into their car and he or she drove me to school. Later, I would find out it was a school board member who had been behind me as I came down the hill.

When I entered the middle school building, Mr. Clark steered me into his office. Concerned about my credit card, I explained what had happened, expecting him to run down to the garage and retrieve it.

Instead, he escorted me to a back room near his office. Being sequestered irritated me because I needed to work on my report cards, and I wasn't that late, and I'd pull the day together if everyone would just leave me alone. The school's resource officer, an armed policeman, blocked the doorway.

Going to the emergency room wasn't a choice. The complex set of circumstances coalesced into meaning. My administrators believed my mistake was a suicide attempt. The louder I tried to explain how wrong they were, the less they listened.

I overheard Mr. Clark talking with a teacher's aide, whose temporary job was ending. She accepted the opportunity to continue her employment as my long-term substitute, an incomprehensible event but such a relief. Then, the secretary drove me to the hospital.

I escaped teaching social studies without having to die.

⁂

The emergency room turned into a nightmare. Allison and then Joel, whom I'd requested the nurse not call, showed up at the hospital. I screamed to a deaf audience in a very controlled manner that I had merely made a mistake with my medication. No one gave me credit for being lucid enough to know what was happening.

Allison tried to reassure me. "It'll be all right, Mom."

Joel witnessed everything.

The doctor of the hour told me the school had requested a tox screen. The district was right to do so, and the results would protect me from accusations of drug or alcohol use, but it still hurt my feelings. Geez, Louise, people! It was just one little white pill taken by mistake with zero intent. Let me sleep for a couple of hours, and I'll be fine, got it?

Torey showed up at the hospital hours later. With kindness and strength, she brooked no argument. "Beth, I need you to take your sick leave."

My face flooded with such relief that I almost smiled. "Whatever you need."

⁂

The day before had been my last day with students. I had turned the lights off and closed my door, ordinary actions ending a stressful day. I couldn't have locked it had I known it was my last.

The pea-soup fog in my brain cleared, and the evening stars emerged from the indigo sky. The hospital released me into the care of Allison.

At home, I reached out to the streetlight on the corner for a reassuring word. It shined its light all around me. I closed my eyes and remembered assuring Sammie she was brave enough. The light withheld its wisdom on the matter.

I stop those who seem to have their lives together to confess myself
lost and inquire of them the way to go, but so often their reply has
been, "Me, too; let's go on together," that I begin to suspect that learning
to walk with one another is not just a means, but part of our goal.
—Arden Georgi Thompson

An Important Question

The holiday season brought back vivid memories of the Christmases I'd shared with Joel. I vacillated between profound dread he'd be absent and exalted hope I'd get to see him. We'd grown closer as the first anniversary of our parting neared. Time and distance had softened harsh memories. Perhaps, he noticed the difference lithium had made in my life.

Choosing a gift occupied my mind. I needed something small, inexpensive, and capable of smashing Joel's hesitation to end our separation with one direct but undetectable hit. I decided to buy beer, none of that wine crap that reeked of Robin's influence.

The phone rang, and I ransacked the couch looking for it. "Ha!" Jen giggled. "I bet Anna you'd be home. She owes me a lunch duty; should've gone for double or nothing."

Trading for lunch duties was a significant transaction at the middle school. I imagined Jen's hesitation to up the ante; no one wanted to risk getting stuck in the cafeteria any more than was required.

"Are you up for a visitor?"

"Things are in shambles."

"I'm sure that's an understatement. See you in an hour or so."

Jen arrived with two large shopping bags in tow. "Got wrapping paper? I've got cookies to trade for some help with my stocking stuffers."

I made tea, and while chatting we wrapped candy, crayons, and coloring books for her granddaughters. We shared Christmas memories of when we were little: stockings that could be opened before our parents got out of bed and hot-chocolate-and-cinnamon-roll breakfasts.

She lifted a weighted vest from one of her shopping bags. "Mr. Clark gave me permission to borrow it over vacation."

My heart dropped. I knew Jen's visit wasn't a social call, but the vest? Embarrassment wrestled with an impulse to put it on. It made me feel calmer, wrapping me in a hug I couldn't give myself.

Jen answered my questions about what had happened while I'd been in the hospital. Torey had taken a vote of confidence in me as a teacher. Jen reached out to touch my hand. "I told her something was really wrong." She sat up straighter and drew in a breath. "Beth, I told her you couldn't do your job." Her eyes darted around, looking for the scissors, as they welled with tears.

"That was the right thing to do, don't give it a second thought! You were honest. As strange as it sounds, I'm grateful." I dropped my eyes, reached for a cookie, and chose a roll of wrapping paper. "I'm glad the charade is over. You know what? The worst that can happen is I have to go live with my aunt in Albuquerque."

Albuquerque may have been a beautiful place to be devastated, but without mania helping me imagine wearing twirly dresses and carrying flower baskets while playing tag with tractor-trailer trucks, the prospect of living with Aunt Elizabeth in the backrooms of a run-down antique store terrified me.

Jen packed the wrapped gifts in her shopping bags. Instead of gathering her coat to go, she reached out her hand and drew me to my feet. "I have something important to ask you."

I anticipated an accusation about how I'd handled myself, and thoughts scrambled to cover my bases before she opened her mouth.

"Would you consider being tested by Dr. Holland?"

Dr. Holland was the pediatric psychologist who'd requested I complete Brian's behavior rating scale, the one who'd worked with our district since I started teaching in 1984. I'd met him only a few times at IEP meetings. I floundered for a second, trying to place him. "Why in the world would I do that?"

"I've been in and out of your classroom all semester; I know how difficult things are for you. If you were one of my students, I'd recommend an evaluation."

"I don't see why."

"Information about a problem is always useful, right? Being evaluated can't make anything worse, and who knows, Dr. Holland might uncover something that will help you."

I trusted Jen and had a gut feeling she was right. Despite Dr. Larsen's help, something was amiss. Jen was one of those magical special educators whose emotional intelligence and integrity changed lives. But I had reservations. The thought of seeing a pediatric psychologist embarrassed me. What if Dr. Holland recognized me from school? What if other teachers found out?

"I'm going to make an appointment for you. I'll keep track of the dates, and Anna will help fill out the paperwork."

"Anna knows?"

Jen shrugged her shoulders and winked. "What can I say? Friends talk about friends." She shrugged on her down jacket. "Do you have plans for Christmas?"

"Joel said he'd be over."

"Should I call?" Jen was direct in asking if I meant to harm myself.

"No. I'm fine."

"Promise?"

"Promise."

⁓

Joel showed up on Christmas morning with cinnamon rolls. We exchanged our small gifts and later feasted on Chinese take-out with beer and tea—an almost perfect day, soured by the unspoken tension of my most recent trip to the emergency room.

◈

At midnight on New Year's Eve, the Waterford crystal ball dropped at Times Square and a million people cheered. I wondered what kind of resolution might stop me from spending my days waiting for time to pass or scrambling to find enough of it to keep up with demands.

Torey had asked for another note from my doctor so she could start another extended sick leave for me. I needed to see Dr. Grant, who wrote one that said I'd be out of the classroom for an indeterminate amount of time. At the end of my brief appointment, Dr. Grant reminded me to be sure to let her know if I had any problems.

◈

On the morning of January 2nd, Ingrid pulled out of her driveway earlier than usual. She faced a long day at school.

My day was headed toward nothing. I imagined explaining photosynthesis to phantoms. Me, the little girl who wanted to be a teacher, had withered. That child had loved colored chalk, Play-Doh, and tempera paint. I had read the school's library, shelf by shelf, cried on the last day of school, and celebrated its beginning in September. The wound was deep. The loss of my classroom hurt like the death of a loved one.

Having a mental illness wasn't like having the flu. No one could flush my behavioral vomit down the toilet. There was no tumor to cut out, nothing to stitch back into place.

Was I responsible for my actions? I couldn't have chosen not to see the angel or demanded that my mind undream writing a book for Dr. Cabrera. My need for colors was like a biological drive to breathe; of course I needed to buy them. A compulsion, not a decision, had led me away from Joel, away from my home. I didn't know how to figure out the difference between being guilty of irresponsibility and being the victim of a disease.

Through the dark days of isolation, an oddity, a peculiarity, emerged. I wanted to live more than ever before. It was as if the angel had given me his armor and sword. I would do whatever it took to breathe life back into my marriage and my career. I wanted a home, not a place to live.

But I seemed less able to function despite the support of lithium. Rats in mazes got out, even if they didn't get the cheese. Frustrated, irritable, sad, with no end in sight, suicide didn't whisper. It mimed theatrically.

⁂

The Challenger, sensitive to pressure on the accelerator, ignored my suggestion to plow into a tree and, instead, drove me to the emergency room.

A nurse walked me from triage to a tiny examining room. "Lights off?"

I nodded.

She brought a warm blanket and closed the door; light crept under its edge.

The rhythmic beeps from someone's monitor became a metronome that timed my breathing. Atomized disinfectant made the air taste bitter. Capable people moved equipment, their muffled footsteps revealing the presence of patients in greater need than me.

The psych ward remained unchanged, although much less welcoming due to the absence of my friends, Caroline and Cinderella's godmother. *Family Circle*'s Halloween edition still sat askew on the side table. Because I was not on a hold, there was no strip search, no fishbowl interview.

I hadn't remembered clean clothes, so I followed the nurse, dressed in the same costume as the last time I was admitted: a dreadful hospital robe over a gown and ugly gripper socks. We passed the med window to an empty room. "I'll get you some scrubs in the morning. For now, try to get some rest."

Late the next morning, a nurse I didn't recognize walked into the lounge and sat next to me. "Dr. Larsen wants to talk with you." It was kind of her to sit before speaking, a gesture acknowledging I was a functioning adult.

I followed her to the same small office and sat on the same narrow metal chair sandwiched between the desk and the wall.

Dr. Larsen, on call again, smiled at me. "Hello, Bethany. How are you doing?"

"I'm fine."

"If you were fine, you wouldn't be here."

This time, instead of wanting to spit in his face, I laughed. "I'm not almost dead this time; I'm just not okay."

Without vocabulary to explain how disconnected from normalcy I was, no brilliant commentary could illuminate the brokenness. "I don't feel right; there's something wrong."

Dr. Larsen either believed me or didn't; I couldn't tell.

"I have the memory of an aphid, you know." Then, I told him I couldn't read. "I know what words are, but they disappear even though they're right in front of me in black and white." I described my frustration. "I spread all of my physics books on the floor in my apartment, and I can see my writing in the margins, but I can't read them—I wrote the damn notes, and I don't know what they say. Not only that, sometimes words don't come out right."

"Tell me about that."

"The first time I noticed, a student had dropped a spoon in the cafeteria. I tried to tell him to pick it up but couldn't find the words, so I said, 'Pick up the thing you wouldn't want to use for spaghetti but would use if you had soup.' Then, the same week, I told my students the yellow motor was coming. Another time, I asked a student if the baby his mother wore belonged to him."

Dr. Larsen looked up to the left, a nonverbal message I recognized as a signal his brain floundered while trying to construct a visual image of the events.

"The bus—it's yellow and has a motor. I was trying to say it was time for dismissal, and the mom was pregnant, you know; she was wearing a baby."

"Do you get confused?"

Should I begin with the Ambien story? When I didn't know if it was day or night, or how I couldn't figure out whether I had started washing my hair or was finished? How I didn't understand why my car key wouldn't open my door at school? Should I describe the cobra? Or perhaps a more mundane example like calling Ingrid because the dryer wouldn't fill with water?

"Bethany, I believe you have diffuse brain trauma."

I didn't understand.

He explained. "What you are describing, the combination of confusion and language difficulties is brain trauma. Your neurons have been overstimulated for so long the dendrites are exhausted. Some are burned out, which causes the connection to stop working. It's like road rash in your brain. You'll have to give it some time before we'll know how much damage will be permanent. If you'd like, I can refer you to a memory program here at the hospital."

I accepted the brochure he offered entitled "*Understanding Memory Loss*." I wanted to flick his ear and tell him I had problems with R-E-A-D-I-N-G but was certain the brochure would be an excellent addition to the pile of mail Joel would go through on Sunday.

Dr. Larsen crossed his leg over his knee. "I'm sorry this happened. You were very sick, and we tried a lot of medications until we found one that would work."

"I did this to myself by refusing lithium?" I felt as if he were guilty of aiding and abetting me in stabbing my brain with tablets, that he should have known better.

"I doubt it, but it certainly didn't help. The process has been going on for a long time. Your reservations about lithium were legitimate and something I had to respect. Brains are the most complex

161

objects in the known universe, and there were no simple solutions. We did the best we could."

"If I were a good person, none of this would have happened."

Dr. Larsen sighed. "You don't have a character defect, Bethany; your brain is running amok." He straightened his tie and turned to his computer. He asked a few questions as he worked his way through a checklist.

"Where are you concerning menopause?"

"It's been a year. I'm finished, I think."

"Menopause can trigger bipolar disorder, you know."

No shit.

Perhaps the finest teachers are those who look at us and
see how wonderful we truly are so that we can be.
—Arden Georgi Thompson

Lessons

I should have shopped around for a different psychiatrist, one who, no matter what, refrained from accessorizing one problem with another, one who wouldn't wrest defeat from the jaws of victory.

But I didn't.

After explaining my brain injury and asking about menopause, Dr. Larsen spoke to me in that off-hand manner people adopt when they don't want to embarrass anyone. "I think we need to look at borderline personality disorder."

I visualized myself as a diseased, disjointed doll with matted hair and dirt on her face, with one eye stuck shut and the other searching for half the world. He may as well have told me I'd been walking around in public with toilet paper hanging out from under my skirt.

Dr. Larsen seemed unaware of my inner earthquake's magnitude. "It means your moods and behavior are volatile and you have trouble managing relationships." He gathered some papers and tapped them into a neat pile. "You don't need to be in the hospital. I'm discharging you to the day-treatment program. They're already expecting you."

Slam dunk, he broke the news and distanced himself. "Good luck, Bethany."

On the way to the outpatient program, I raged at the unfairness of life by turning up the car stereo and blasting folk songs from the center of the universe into the farthest reaches of my sphere of influence. Lithium had proved a difficult pill to swallow; what was next? A body cast around my aura?

⁂

On the third morning of the hospital's outpatient program, Yoga Girl's apparition perched on the table. She wore a cat-ate-the-canary grin. In front of me was a list of mindfulness activities. Her transparent finger pointed to the list: learning a new yoga pose and taking a bubble bath. Her earnest, ghostly voice taunted me. *Told ya so; a salute to the sun followed by a bubble bath will turn your day around.*

Only the occupational therapist saw through my ruse about stepping out for coffee. "Wait." She ducked away, then returned and slipped me a business card. "Call her; she's the right one for you."

I left the hospital's program with an unorthodox recommendation for a new therapist.

⁂

The business card's address led me to Alice.

Her practice was located in her home, a crooked New Englander built during the Civil War. The yard, bounded by a weathered picket fence, was a mishmash of mud and snow. Two gnarled deciduous trees threatened the roof. They'd survived a hundred years of nor'easters, but there was no sure bet their luck would hold.

Near the expansive porch, an older woman in hot-pink rubber boots and a frayed woolen coat cracked a good-sized log in half with her splitting ax. Long braided hair coiled atop her head like a silver coronet. The Snow Queen in a Paul Bunyan disguise glanced my way.

The scene made me doubt my sanity. I'd left home for my appointment expecting to find a generic office building staffed by a huffy receptionist and cookie-cutter mental health providers.

I slowed my car to a crawl. The number on her house matched the one on the business card, but she didn't look like a licensed clinical social worker. She looked sort of—*right*. I detected no hint of a scowl, or question, or evaluation in her face as she returned my gaze.

I pulled to the side of the road and stopped my car to decide whether to ask a question or run.

The woman set the ax against her knee and arched her back. "Are you looking for me?"

Alice's front door opened into a mudroom with a floor of unfinished hardwood sanded to softness by a hundred years of grit scuffed underfoot. "Hang your coat here." She stepped on the backs of her pink boots to remove them and tossed them into the corner.

She stuffed small logs into a wood stove already so hot whorls of air lifted from its surface.

I claimed a cabbage-rose upholstered chair situated nearby, hoping to melt the dread that made my knees shiver.

Alice heaved an overstuffed binder out from under her worn rocker onto her lap "What do you know about DBT?"

"Nothing."

She dug for a handout. "DBT stands for Dialectic Behavioral Therapy. Do you know what a dialectic is?"

I shook my head. I'd never heard the word before.

"A dialectic is something that can be thought about in different ways. I'll bet I'm an example. Do you have mixed emotions about being here?"

"Terribly." I needed help but wanted to get back in my car and peel out of her driveway.

"That's the way of it. DBT offers a way to explore complicated issues in logical ways."

That appealed to me. Over the course of our first hour, Alice explained the program. I needed to commit to a year's study of skills related to emotional regulation, interpersonal relationships, and distress tolerance.

She laid out rules I'd have to follow if I agreed to be her client. "First, don't call me during a crisis; call 911 if you need help. I'll talk with you for as long as you need before or afterward, but not during. We'll meet each week for a private session until I deem it unnecessary."

How could I refuse? I recognized a teacher with a curriculum when I saw one.

⁂

Alice opened our first therapy session with a question that seemed to have a simple answer. "Who are you?"

"I'm a teacher."

"That is what you do. I asked who you are."

Experience taught me to tell my abused-child story to therapists, so I began with the nightly entertainment I provided to my father.

Alice ripped the rug out from under me. "I don't want to hear your story."

"But it's a really good one!" I felt robbed; I had been rehearsing so I'd finally be able to tell it without crying.

"I'm sure it is. We won't use the past to build the future."

Stunned and silent, brought up short, I realized that was the smartest thing I'd ever heard a therapist say. Alice threw a lifeline when she cut me off; I clung to it and moved forward.

⁂

One of my homework assignments required me to practice a skill called STOP: *s*top, *t*ake a breath, *o*bserve, and *p*roceed during difficult situations. I was to go out to dinner and a movie—alone.

A diner featured tall-backed booth seating for extra privacy, down-home cooking with no weird ingredients, and no margaritas on the menu. Once I was seated, the waitress climbed on the table and turned on the neon sign flashing *Look Who's Here Alone*. I left a twenty to cover a grilled cheese sandwich, no fries, to ensure I needn't interact with the waitress, then fled to my car.

At the movie theater, I left my car at the farthest end of the parking lot, away from people. While standing in line for a ticket, I realized how stupid that was—when the movie ended, I'd need to cross the parking lot alone, so I left the ticket line to relocate my car.

Returning to the ticket booth, the girl behind the Plexiglas asked which movie I wanted to see.

Good question! I hadn't thought that far ahead. Someone, somewhere, said the word *three,* so I echoed it. "Three, please." That is how I found myself in the third dark cavernous theater venue to watch *The Conjuring,* a supernatural horror movie based on the Warren family's real-life experiences in the nearby state of Rhode Island.

To make matters worse, I chose the wrong seat. Being in the center usually protected me from those needing to buy popcorn or visit the restroom. At this moment, a half-hour into the movie, I was stuck in the middle. The horror on the screen collided with the horror of making a scene as I escaped. I drove past rising bodies that threatened me even though people were helping by moving out of my way. My brain careened through the blackness, the scalloped rope of the seatbacks guiding me, Alice's ghost reminding me to **S-T-O-P**, but I ignored everything and ran, my breath locked inside my chest.

⌒

Alice listened as I recounted my adventure replete with tears. "You're whining—it's unproductive."

Yup. Hundreds of hours listening to parents and teachers had taught me that describing problems over and over did nothing to help anyone, although it did vent frustration.

"Do you remember what I taught you about fear?"

I rolled my eyes and regurgitated information using a sing-song voice. "Fear raises awareness and is a signal to be vigilant."

"And?"

"And, supposedly, I will respond appropriately if there is real danger, or use one of the skills to tolerate discomfort if there isn't."

Alice paused. "The danger of going to the movies isn't real at this moment."

The bloody hell it wasn't. It was so real I sat in the chair, gagged and tied, eyeballs bulging beyond the tip of my nose.

Alice butted into my panic. "Look. Everyone has emotions; think about people as if they were horses. Some trudge along as if they are tired old farm plugs; some are prancing ponies. Surely you know someone like that! Most people are the ones you'd find in any barn in the country. You, my dear, are a destrier, a knight's mighty charger."

I considered that emotions differed genetically as did height, eye color, and intelligence. I conceded that one to Alice. My intense emotions *did* loom large and were hard to control. Joel? To me, Joel was a mighty Clydesdale, stoic, even-tempered, and steady, an evenly matched opposite of a destrier.

Alice allowed me to think while she made some tea. She set a mug on the coffee table and waited until I re-engaged. "Beth, you aren't holding the reins, and you missed the saddle."

A sip of tea splashed down my trachea. The hysterical image was accurate. That was me, all right, bouncing up and down on the ass of an enormous horse hellbent on jumping off a cliff, with both hands clinging to the saddle horn, my legs working to shift my body forward onto the seat, all the while whipping the reins clenched in my mouth trying to change my destrier's direction. Yup.

At least lithium turned my charger's head away from the cliff.

"Stop thinking about your emotions—it's counterproductive. Did you know I keep a snake under your chair?"

I tripped over my coat on the way through the door.

Alice joined me outside. "The idea of a snake made you afraid; fear grabbed your attention. Then you got angry, which took you out the door. Just like at the theater."

I evaluated her. Bitch, she teaches like I do, kicking students into the deep end, knowing they can swim.

"Come on, sit with me. I wouldn't keep a snake in my house. I don't like them, either."

We returned to the room, but I didn't sit in the cabbage-rose upholstered chair ever again.

"Look, your emotions made you act; you knew what to do. Now, your thinking is revisiting the event, causing it to happen again. Your fear isn't even about the snake or the movie anymore. You wonder what else is lurking. You're evaluating my honesty; you're embarrassed; any number of things are on your mind."

Damn it.

"The only time your emotions were real today was when I told you a falsehood. There is nothing in this room but your screaming brain. Can you understand how this pattern has taken over your life? Your brain is popping popcorn while it's watching a horror movie."

God love the eloquent lady.

"Look, you can't change the past, and you'll never change who you are, but you can learn to deal with your feelings. It won't happen overnight, but you can gain control if you use DBT skills. I'll teach you the difference between sadness and depression and how to grieve. I'll help you understand the distinction between guilt and shame."

She reached out and touched my knee. "You know better than anyone learning takes time. Stop thinking; your first step is to do something, anything, in a new way. Don't let your feelings pop out of control. When the first kernel snaps, stop. Identify the emotion. Attend to it correctly. Remember? You don't want to make a secondary mess and then have to clean that up too."

The following week I took an unfamiliar route to Alice's house. I was doing something, anything, *differently*. Of course, I got lost.

The simple change earned me a stern talking to because I arrived late. Then, Alice and I sipped another cup of tea to celebrate the victory.

It tasted awful; disgust curled one side of my lip.

"When you get better with the skills, I'll serve better tea. Now, what flavors did you notice, and which ones didn't you like?"

She had slipped bitters and peppermint oil into my mug. Mindfulness. She was teaching me mindfulness. "Not paying much attention to your falling-apart world, now, are you? Everything's fine. Have a cookie."

"No, thank you."

Once bitten, twice shy.

❧

I arrived at another therapy session out of sorts, in no mood for anything, feeling put upon and less impressed with life than usual. "I'm having the worst day of my life."

"Joan of Arc can show up on my doorstep and tell me she is having the *worst* day of her life. You can't." She snapped her fingers. "Rephrase."

❧

Lesson Seventeen changed my life. Alice had uncoiled her coronet so that her thick gray braid reached her lap. Her hair was tied with a leather thong, and she was barefoot. There was no doubt in my teacher's mind she'd dressed for the occasion. I imagined her young, certain she'd have walked with those protesting the Vietnam war, a staunch feminist fighting for the cause.

The crooked photocopy she handed me surfaced a pet peeve: I found teachers who provided inferior materials to students and then expected them to return first-rate products to be hypocrites of the highest degree. "Put a lot of time into this one, did you? I'd be happy to take your book and make a new master."

Her divining rod didn't falter. "This lesson is about radical acceptance. Here's your chance."

The concept of radical acceptance demanded I extend compassion to my inner critic that nattered on and on, the one who predicted gloom and doom, second by second. It loved me, so it used negativity to protect me because I was its best and only friend.

Extending kindness from me to my *self* differed from former therapists' advice. Once, I had decided to love my parents no matter what, even though I disliked them. Did Alice insinuate I'd do that for my *self*? Love me no matter what, even though I disliked myself thoroughly?

Alice ran her hand across her copy of the workbook. We discussed one dimension of borderline personality disorder. "Look, you want something you can't have, and you need to figure out that isn't a catastrophe."

Damn it, she'd identified another truth. I'd been lying since grade school, pretending to have what I didn't.

Alice tossed her braid over her shoulder and pulled her foot onto the chair, clasping her leg. She looked like a flower child listening to Bob Dylan. "Marsha Linehan developed DBT because of her own experiences. Radical acceptance is an idea that comes from the Buddhists. She learned about it while staying at a monastery in Southern California to study with the monks." Alice resettled her foot to the floor. "You grew up in Montana. Do you know Chief Joseph?"

"He was the Nez Perce warrior who said I shall fight no more forever."

"Yes. He came to a full stop without failure and allowed honor to transcend the events that caused his people's brokenness. Radical acceptance doesn't imply forgiveness or that you ignore the unacceptable or deny the undeniable."

My back stiffened and my throat knotted. Could I, too, fight no more forever? Might I be a beautiful antique with cracked veneer or wormhole edges, a scarred object worthy of love? I tried to express the idea that emerged. "Do you mean I can find honor instead of healing?"

"Yes, you have to accept reality. Quit managing your image and figure out you can't be perfect. I'm not your fairy godmother, and you don't get to be Cinderella."

"Do you lie awake at night thinking this stuff up?"

"Sometimes."

Without courage to fail nothing new is ever tried; then we like flightless birds rely on feet alone and forget what joy it was to fly.
—Arden Georgi Thompson

The Starfish

To: Bethany Davis
> From: Torey Blake, Assistant Superintendent
> Subject: How can we support you?

> Can we meet on Wednesday? I'll be in my office all morning, so stop by at your convenience. We'll talk about moving forward into the upcoming school year and how to best support you as we make some changes.
> Torey

～

Finally, a smidgen of hope. All I needed was to avoid social studies, the cafeteria, and the playground. Oh, and, if possible, I'd avoid any student who screamed at the top of their lungs with veins standing out in purple ropes and sweat gathering on their brow. I deserved a safe work environment. Who would protect me?

Last year, I climbed the administrative building's steps like a starfish hoping for one more wave to tumble her back to familiar rocks. This time, I climbed the stairs clinging to Torey's encouraging words. I needed ninety days, just one more semester, to reach the state's threshold for early retirement. There'd be no social security to fall back on as state employees paid into the state's retirement fund.

Torey's office door was open, and my file sat squarely in the middle of her desk. She stood near the window and pinched spent blooms from her African violets while looking out over the parking lot. After greeting me, she said the strangest thing. "This is the part of my job I hate."

I knew she didn't mean deadheading violets.

While I settled into a nearby chair, Torey pulled a pencil from behind her ear, set it on her desk, then picked it up and put it back behind her ear. She didn't mince words. "Beth, I can't put you back in the classroom next year."

Torey's e-mail hadn't meant she'd support my return; she meant to support me as I left. How could I have misunderstood? I pictured telling Joel about my failure and imagined his face, sure he'd remain silent. I melted into a puddle of shame as if she were Dorothy with a bucket of watery reality and I were the Wicked Witch of the West. I imagined myself homeless, a real possibility as I lived paycheck to paycheck. I had no savings because I still struggled to pay off credit card debt. I couldn't live in my apartment as Ingrid's guest.

Needles of terror prickled under my skin. "One semester, Torey, ninety days, that's all I need. If I don't get the time, I'll lose my retirement." My eyes squeezed shut, not wanting to look reality in the eye. "What am I going to do?"

Torey looked away.

I pitied her. This was the part of her job she hated, and no wonder. Was she right to remove me from my position? Absolutely. Teachers must be able to meet their students' needs. I could not. I wondered how to make terminating my employment easier for her.

"It's okay, Torey. Every day I thought I'd wake up and things would be back to normal."

The sticky wicket was that my illness and brain injury had unfurled slowly, a medical emergency that didn't have a clear beginning or a definitive end. It was hidden from sight and took an unfamiliar path.

Torey paced. "Be honest. If I assigned you to a classroom, could you do your job?"

I had one more year's worth of sick leave in my bank, so I lied to save my ass. "Yes."

"Then why haven't you been?"

There it was. The question I'd been asking myself. Frightening. Threatening. Revealing.

I returned her gaze. What the hell had happened to me? I was a chimney standing in the rubble of a raging fire that obliterated the structure around it. "I got sick, and my brain got hurt." I spilled what it was like trying to teach while not being able to read, not being able to call a human being by name. "I still can't read, and I can't remember anything."

"I know."

I felt nothing but relief bookended by terror. I wanted to take on a great dare without the ability to win. Who was this incompetent stranger who looked like me but was not? Reality shifted, and I became an animal about to be put down. I watched as Torey moved to grasp my arm, ready to jab me with a lethal injection. But no, it was her hand reaching for mine, and she held a pencil, not a syringe.

I was collateral damage. There was no evidence the stress of the "Brian year" impacted the sloth-paced catastrophe that injured me even though I believed it had affected my mental health. That shock could never be quantified or teased apart from bipolar disorder.

I thought about Alice's lesson about radical acceptance and pictured Chief Joseph in my mind. I decided, like him, I would fight no more forever. What other choice was there? Hands clasped as if in prayer, I closed my eyes and told the truth. "We both know I lied; I can't do any better." My chin quivered, and biting my lip didn't stop the tears. "I've been trying so hard."

Torey moved to sit near me and rested her hand on mine. "I know. We knew you needed help, but no one knew what to do."

"I'll clean bathrooms, Torey. Anything. I'm going to lose my retirement." My legs started to tremble. "I can't start another career; I'm almost sixty!" I didn't tell her I'd applied at Walmart but was

175

too qualified to stock shelves. Or about being turned down for disability twice. "I won't be anything anymore."

"You'll always be a teacher, Beth. No one can take that away."

School held me steady in a way Joel never could. My narrow and intense focus on natural and mathematical systems landed me in a niche where I excelled without effort. Classrooms were isolated islands I was perfectly suited to inhabit.

Torey opened my file and pulled out my commendations. She was silent for a long time. "I've got an idea. Do you remember the website we were going to build?"

Did I remember? Creating it was my brainchild; I envisioned an online hub to organize the science curriculum at each grade level. It would allow users to set up an interactive library of teacher-created, peer-reviewed materials, resources, and common assessments. My vision was to have a dozen ways to teach gravity or light or cells instead of adhering to a one-size-fits-all science program.

Just talking about the site with Torey was enough to mask the upset. "I'm going to talk to Mark. Stay here."

Several moments later, a movement outside the window captured my attention. A bald eagle had landed on a tree and began to preen its feathers. Such an extraordinary sight, and it appeared without the magic of mania. I believed my warrior angel had settled in to wait with me. I remembered his message: *Know this—the darkness is not real.*

Mark and Torey returned and asked if I'd accept a half-time position as a technology specialist.

I tearfully agreed, utterly spent.

Torey dispensed tissues. "There's no office space for you at the middle school. Would you be willing to work at the Alt School?"

The Alternative School was Torey's brainchild, a self-contained program for students poised on the brink of failure. Most had been expelled from the district and were involved with the juvenile justice system. She located it in the first building I'd taught in almost thirty years ago. Only an archangel could have brought me full circle to end my career at a desk situated in my original classroom.

Mark told me he'd have to take the proposal to the school board for approval but was confident they'd agree. Instead of a doctor's note, I was required to submit a postdated letter of resignation effective at the end of the school year. Essentially, I wouldn't be fired provided I quit.

I thought about the board member who had taken me to school with shampoo in my hair that day when I drove the Challenger off the road. I doubted I had a snowball's chance in hell of being hired to build a website.

Writing a letter of resignation made me think about the hours before I reached out to touch the truck. My career would end before its natural conclusion, and I had to leave a note.

I wrote:

Dear Mr. Hughes,
    Please accept my resignation from my position as a seventh-grade classroom teacher effective August 31, 20—.
    Your support before, during, and after my illness changed my life, and always for the better. Whether allowing me time away for professional development or assisting me while I couldn't function in my classroom, your kindness and integrity reflected the highest standard of professionalism. It has been an honor to be a member of your staff.
    I feel a great sense of loss as I withdraw from the school district I love.
    Sincerely,
    Bethany L. Davis

I'd been granted one last semester, which would be the last autumn rising to greet winter, which would fall into spring that ebbed into perpetual summer, the loneliest time of the year.

Each creature has a right to be without explanation
or apology just because it is. And so do we.
—Arden Georgi Thompson

Assessments

J oel asked me on a date to celebrate my birthday. A near-by bikers'
bar had always been one of those destinations that fascinated me.
My gift was his escort into its nether regions. In the mid-afternoon,
Joel's big black Dodge truck rumbled into the parking lot behind
three Harleys.

I was fifty-eight but felt sixteen when I stepped down from his
truck dressed in a khaki blazer over a white blouse tucked into my
size six jeans. My look featured a wide leather belt and Frye square-
toe harness boots, not spiked heels.

Joel ordered a beer for himself and an oversized basket of waffle
fries for us to share. We maneuvered through a sea of people dressed
in cut leather vests until we found an empty patio table nested in
tawny, late summer grass. The August heat had let up, and the afternoon sun turned everything into a new start.

A frightfully familiar voice rose above the crowd. "Hey, there
they are."

My nose crinkled. Hugh and Robin closed in. The ripple of
heads moving out of the way reminded me of a two-headed grass
snake pushing its way through the lawn.

"Haven't seen you for so long!" Robin stooped to hug me.

What a shame that changed! I eyed Joel. Was this meeting
planned or a coincidence?

With drinks in hand, Hugh settled in near Joel.

Robin scooted in beside me and ran her eyes up and down my figure, again not bothering to hide her evaluation or surprise. "You look *really* good."

At that moment, I was grateful I'd spent the last year puking with anxiety and mourning the absence of Joel. I'd lost thirty pounds, and I was enjoying every second of it. I kept my mouth shut and smiled.

"Happy birthday, by the way!"

Ah, the woman knew. The pipeline between her and Joel hadn't closed. I'd always been protective of my birthday, and no matter the number of times I asked for it to be a private affair, others seemed to think their presence enhanced my experience.

Robin zeroed in. "Aren't you glad you didn't make a permanent decision to solve a temporary problem?"

A fucking poster slogan? I'd almost ripped the placard with that trite saying off the wall at the workshop I had attended after saying goodbye to Sammie. A temporary problem, my ass. My psychological pain was intractable.

The catchphrase echoed. Joel had voiced those exact words not more than a week ago. The slogan evoked a carnival huckster's image shouting: Hey, bud, buy a free ticket and join the queue! We've got pat answers sure to soothe.

Joel and Hugh engaged in conversation while Robin droned at me in a tone that resonated like curling ribbon drawn across scissors. "Only selfish cowards take the easy way out."

According to Robin, mental illness was fake and a cover-up for irresponsibility. She called me childish, selfish, and weak, then switched to a caring demeanor and patted my arm. "Just think positive thoughts like me." She turned the dagger in my back. "How are you getting by?"

"I've used most of my sick leave; I only have another 180 days in my bank."

"My dad taught me never to take a dime I didn't earn."

I refrained from explaining my contract.

Her blue-edged diamond flashed as she fingered her necklace. She shook her head and rolled her eyes. "I wouldn't be able to hold my head up if I were you." She smiled and pulled at her straw.

Sinking into the Earth's core couldn't have distanced me far enough from her shaming words. I had no doubt she and Joel had discussed me. Did he politely and superficially exchange words with her, or did he share her beliefs? If they shared the same perspective, how could he give me such support? And, if he disagreed, how could he engage with her?

Robin joined Hugh and Joel's conversation about their employees and recycling metal turnings. The three of them, tightly enmeshed, talked about important matters.

I left them to their business, my mood and stomach churning. In a moment of brilliance, I grinned at Robin while slowly sliding a fry into my mouth, then slid the plate her way and passed the ketchup.

Robin edged away, rested her elbow on the table, and kept me in her line of sight. "Did you use the books you bought in D.C.? You were so excited about them!"

Bitch! Add some pepper to the salt you just threw in my wound! "I donated them to the school." Timidity and good manners kept me from backhanding her.

Had I been diagnosed with cancer or lost a leg to diabetes, would Robin have shamed me? Perhaps she would have asked what she could do to help or sent a card.

The worst of it, though? More than half of me wondered if she were right.

After Labor Day, I returned to school, not as a teacher but as a specialist who would create the website I'd conceptualized. Jesse's ghost, trapped in time as a sixth grader, waited for me inside the same classroom first assigned to me in 1984. Almost thirty years later, his hushed memory suggested I place my desk in his spot, the farthest corner to the right of the wooden door.

I flat-out admired Jesse. He personified my alter ego who possessed the courage to rage against malevolence rather than run from it. His brilliant spirit, his tenacity, and his unflinching self-confidence had turned him into a Goliath-slayer in my eyes.

I'd heard him before I met him. The first yellow bus pulled up to the school, and something exploded out of the folding doors. "Fuckin' bus driver didn't give a crap about missing me. I'm gonna fuckin' kick his ass."

Jesse had arrived.

The other teachers had rolled their eyes while my hand fluttered to the center of my chest. It was my first day, and my vision of meeting students was more genteel.

Many students were curious about me, the new teacher they needed to size up.

When Jesse pushed to the front of the small throng of children, he stopped short and stared at me, an appalled expression on his face. "You might want to change laundry detergent."

Mrs. Porter, a veteran teacher, stepped in. "That one. Make sure he takes his hat off when we go inside." Her varmint-hunting face reminded me of Elmer Fudd looking down his double-barrel shotgun at a *wascally wabbit*. "He's not getting away with it."

That year after Christmas vacation, Jesse was absent. I missed watching the daily battle between his iron will and Mrs. Porter's convictions. Jesse hadn't returned to school because he was in AMHI, the Augusta Mental Health Institute, after trying to commit suicide.

His distress wasn't mine to understand. Each day, I sent him a short letter telling him about school events and enclosed a stamp, a piece of gum, or a word puzzle. I never asked him why his world was too heavy to bear.

On one particularly stressful day, after he'd returned to school, a teacher on the playground severed his proverbial Achilles' heel. He raged as he stormed into the classroom. "Mrs. Michaels called my sister a retard, so I punched her in the face."

His heart tore apart in front of me. He had protected what he loved and was in trouble for it.

"Come on; I'll talk to the principal later. Tell me what happened."

I knew there was more to the story because no teacher, especially Mrs. Michaels, would say such a thing.

"Tell me what happened before you hit her."

"I asked her why Olivia had to be in Miss Becky's class and she said Olivia's a slow learner. That's the same as bein' a retard, ya know."

It wasn't the right time to explain; he was too upset to listen. I graded papers while tense minutes passed.

Jesse exploded from his desk, grabbed his chair, and hurled it across the room, narrowly missing the wavy glass of the old window. The force gouged the wooden frame.

I stared at the wood's white wound in confusion. I neared Jesse, whose sobs shook his body, and gently cupped his face with my hands. I gazed into his eyes as if I were holding a crystal ball. "I'll tell Mr. Cyr how much you love Olivia. We'll find a better way to protect her than hitting someone. Okay?"

Decades later, touching the blemish in the window's frame evoked a sense of déjà vu. Over time, the aged scar had become as indiscernible as I felt. As a part-time employee, I had no reason to be at school on the first day, but I couldn't miss the spectacle. Two naive second-year special education teachers pitted themselves against a student body comprised of the highest order of survivors.

Mr. Cyr's ghost joined me. He leaned against the left door frame, and I leaned against the right.

He sized up the two new teachers, one an ex-Marine who believed in discipline and the other a dreamer who believed in children. "Who do you think will win?"

I examined the demeanor of the two men. "I bet on the dreamer."

Mr. Cyr faded away.

The bus arrived, and its driver was the first to enter the building. "Little shits. You can't pay me enough!" He dropped the keys to the bus into the ex-Marine's hand and headed toward the office to call his wife for a ride home.

The students whooped in victory.

The teachers exchanged determined looks.

I withdrew and closed my door.

In October, red winterberries fell from a rambling bush onto my lowest porch step. Joel's boot burst their cells when he stepped on them. The pigments that shot out of the fragile tissue left a crimson stain on the worn boards—a blood-oath between us. His dearest face looked through the screen door. "Anyone home?"

I'd heard the truck and was already on my way. "Me, me, me!"

Time had reset to when we were young and filled with hope, back to those years when reality was vibrant and promising. Joel's presence erased bad things. My strength combined with his, and calmed by his calmness, I held on for dear life. "Joel, I love you."

His shirt smelled of coolant from his milling machine and laundry soap. "I love you too, girl."

We talked for hours, coming full circle to the problem set into stone when I was ill and flying toward the sun.

"I'm scared things will get bad again."

"No more, Beth. It's done; we'll move on."

This time, we stepped into cause and consequence together, thinking we could pick up from where we'd started decades before. Our wedding rings slid back on our fingers. With no ceremony to mark the occasion, we agreed to live together again. He gave me a lingering kiss on the forehead and said the words I was dying to hear. "Go ahead, look for a place for us."

Recalling the incident on the stair landing when he'd arrived with his bed made me freeze. I'd sworn never to feel happy again, so I waited until he left before dancing off to find boxes.

An old farmhouse was for sale in a nearby town and, approved for a mortgage, we moved all of our belongings once more.

Joel, a machinist by trade who was measured, held his tolerances, and deburred every word before uttering it assured me my choice was fine. But, he longed for the opposite: something new, built with precision, a blank canvas with no reminders. He didn't fight to get his way.

The white house represented me; it had good bones but it sagged and begged for a do-over; it had potential but only if loved. Its scarred walls revealed its history. The house reached out and welcomed me into itself.

The mighty destrier and the steadfast Clydesdale slid into their harnesses and took their places, back to back, ready for the final pull.

⁂

In November, eleven months after Jen had made an appointment with Dr. Holland, the phone rang. Sure it was Joel, I spoke flippantly. "You'd better be someone I want to talk to!"

"Is this Bethany?"

The use of the formal version of my name never boded well.

"Oops, I'm sorry. Yes, it is."

"I'm Dr. Holland's receptionist. We've had a cancellation. Would you be able to come in earlier?"

Dr. Holland? I'd forgotten about him altogether. The new date worked, so I accepted the appointment.

Two days later, a thick envelope arrived in the mail. I recognized the behavior rating scale as the same one I'd filled out for Brian. This time I completed it about myself.

On November 17th, I crossed the bridge over the river and parked my car in the psychologist's graveled lot. His practice was located on the second floor of an 1800s Greek Revival building. The opportunity to investigate the architecture was almost worth the doctor's fee.

I waited in a dingy second-floor alcove, a disappointment because the back staircase didn't allow a glimpse into the imposing building. The floor, covered in decaying indoor-outdoor carpet, reeked of dust and wet foam padding with overtones of floral-perfumed carpet freshener.

A young man approached. He fiddled with his tie before he spoke. "We only have one of the children's rooms available. Will that be okay?"

"I prefer it; I'm used to sitting at children's tables."

He led me to a room lifted out of a school and transplanted into the sea captain's home. A round classroom table circled by a few tiny chairs sat in the center atop dull beige linoleum tiles. Battered pine shelving painted with primary colors held a worn cluttered collection of testing materials.

"Let me get you a different chair."

"No, please don't. I like this one."

The courage of the children who had sat at it surrounded me. I imagined a thousand little people crowded into the room. Had they been as anxious as I? Were they determined to get every question correct? Did they want to swipe the testing materials off the table? Did they feel small?

The young man repeatedly tightened his tie, then tugged at his collar to loosen it, readying himself to administer the battery of performance tasks. He took a red binder from the shelf and read the instructions for the children's version of the Wechsler Intelligence Scale aloud.

Flushed with embarrassment, he conceded his mistake. "I need the adult version." He excused himself and returned with another red binder, a second copy of the children's version.

Confusion played across his face as he compared the notebook in his hand with the one on the table. They were identical. "I can't believe I did that." He talked to the floor. "I need the blue one. I'll be right back."

I recognized the difference between inexperience and incompetence. With more practice, I knew his nervousness would solidify into expertise. "It's okay; I've done worse." I stifled my desire to laugh, not at him but at the memory of my own faux pas. He inspired my trust despite bungling the binders. I doubted he'd ever had an adult choose to stay in the children's room, and the change in routine introduced a speed bump into his thinking.

At the close of the second eight-hour day of testing, my back was stiff and my brain fog was pea-soup thick.

He reassured me with a dismissive remark. "Everyone gets tired; it'll be okay."

No wonder students who returned to the classroom after this process were tired and cranky. Bless our hearts.

If I tell you where I hurt, or let you see what brings tears to my eyes,
will you move in to destroy me, or like any other sane animal in
Earth's kingdom, acknowledge our mutuality by lowering your eyes?
—Arden Georgi Thompson

Lowered Eyes

One year after Jen made the appointment, I finally met Dr. Holland. The esteemed pediatric psychologist looked like John Lennon dressed in an Edwardian suit. The effect was disconcerting, a curious meld of a long-haired hippie with a stuffy aristocratic gentleman.

Within his office, the scent of cherry-flavored tobacco, dark roast coffee, and saddle-soaped leather lent the space a masculine feeling. Small logs crackled in the massive fireplace. I couldn't help but compare the ostentatious room with that of the testing area.

At fifty-eight years of age, it was my turn to be evaluated, summarized, and re-labeled.

The doctor didn't indicate where I should sit, so I chose to tuck myself into the corner of a tufted leather couch by the windows rather than the small, upholstered chair near the door. Outside the window, the ice-rimmed river was visible. The whine of tires changed pitch as cars crossed the old bridge's expansion joints, evoking a desire to run away too.

The doctor sat in a leather wingback chair situated between the fireplace and his desk. He extended a copy of my test results, forcing me to rise to take it from his hand. With practiced fingers, he swirled his rose-colored round glasses, rolling the ear loops between his deft fingers.

The verdict. Hopefully, the test results showed no trace of borderline personality disorder or lithium in the system and would confirm I'd returned to the land of the sane.

"I'm going to read your evaluation aloud. If you have questions, stop me, and I will answer them."

An amber-hued antique Tiffany lamp sat beside the wing chair, and the hardwood floor was covered by a Prussian blue Aubusson rug. Sunlight played along its shimmering silken fibers in a way that suggested it was an antique worth more than my car. The papers rested in my lap as I closed my eyes and listened as the evidence presented itself in the numbers. The findings showed I was gifted in some areas with measurable discrepancies in others.

Dr. Holland turned the last sheet to its original position, then twisted the stapled papers into a cone.

"...Asperger syndrome."

I tried to formulate a response, but my brain disobeyed. How could that have escaped my attention? If anyone should have known, it was me; I was the freakin' teacher. To distance myself, I reached down to run my fingers across the Prussian blue color. "Is it real?"

Dr. Holland nodded but didn't intrude. Perhaps he knew I couldn't enter into a dialogue; too many contradictory thoughts stumbled over each other. Truth wove through my brain like water finds its way around stones. For thirty years, I had struggled to explain this mystery to my therapists with as much success as a colorblind person trying to explain red.

Dr. Holland scooted forward on his chair. He reversed the curl of the cone in his hand and breached the silence. "Do you know what autism is?"

My brain wrestled with semantics. What does it mean to know? I was *aware* of autism and Asperger syndrome in the same way I was aware of attention deficit disorder, hyperactivity, dyslexia, and physical disabilities. I was *aware*, but I didn't *know* anything. I couldn't fathom what it meant to carry the burden.

Or could I? The diagnosis of Asperger syndrome seemed right; I felt it in my gut. But surely Asperger syndrome wasn't the same as autism, was it? Fear drove an electric spear through my physical body. I'd met autism in person. My vocal cords tightened, causing my one-syllable response to sound like a grasshopper's woeful lament. "Yes."

Autism was Mattie.

❦

Fall Semester, Sophomore Year
Exceptionality 201, Classroom Observation Assignment

Scarlet-leaved maples flanked the front sidewalk of the old elementary school. Wide central stairs with concrete balustrades led to the main entrance, and the double doors opened onto a hardwood floor buffed to a looking-glass finish. The smell of clay and paper conjured a memory of belonging—of safety.

The school secretary, little more than a smile hiding under a mop of black hair curling in every direction, moved toward the reception desk. "What can I help you with, sweetie?"

"I'm Beth from the university to do my observation. Dr. Kratzer partnered me with Miss Mackenzie."

"Oh! I've been keeping an eye out for you." She extended her hand.

"I'm early; Miss Mackenzie isn't expecting me until one."

"She isn't a stickler for time. Sign in and grab a visitor's pass." The secretary pointed to the stairs. "Down one flight, turn left, three doors down."

Miss Mackenzie, a veteran special education teacher with salt-and-pepper hair wearing sneakers and jeans, opened the door when I knocked. She smiled and motioned me in. To my left, a three-foot iguana, sitting on the floor outside its cage, raised its crest. Something warm and moving reached out to clasp my hand and tugged me into the classroom.

At that moment, I became a teacher, unflinchingly eye-to-eye with a large, green reptile while some unknown living thing wrapped around my fingers. The mysterious entity resolved into a little girl with blue eyes and unlaced shoes, the only student apparent in the tiny classroom.

"That's Henry. He won't hurt cha." She pulled me toward a low, round table. "Wanna use my crayons? Wanna sit with me? Wanna see my folder? Wanna go outside with us?"

I sat opposite the chatterbox at a low table. Miss Mackenzie joined us. "Jade Ann, you did a great job welcoming our guest."

The little girl grinned.

Miss Mackenzie looked my way. "I'm going to let you two get acquainted while I talk to Mattie."

Jade Ann boasted about her artwork on the bulletin board. Next, she opened her folder. "See here?" She pointed to a line at the top of her worksheet. "This is where you write your name." Her tongue traced the letters in the air as she wrote.

Miss Mackenzie crouched near the bookshelf at the far end of the room. Before Jade Ann finished the second *n* of her name, a small boy emerged from his hiding spot. Miss Mackenzie responded by returning to the table, giving him autonomy over his decision to join us.

Mattie's most striking attribute was his body language. He crossed his arms and buried his hands in his armpits, a living cartoon of an angry thundercloud.

Jade Ann continued, patting the chair next to her. "Do ya wanna sit over here? Here, pick a color. Don't ya wanna?" She turned to Miss Mackenzie and tugged at her teacher's arm to get her attention. "I'm bein' nice. Why don't she wanna be over here? Don't that lady like me?"

Henry, the iguana, swaggered by the table. His rounded parrot-like claws clicked on the tile.

Mattie mimicked the iguana's awkward gait and pulled his chair closer to his teacher before he sat down.

Miss Mackenzie turned. "Hey, Mr. Mattie, it's nice to see you."

With no warning, a guttural, primordial howl expressing indecipherable terror erupted from the boy.

I froze, horrified and helpless.

Jade Ann gripped the edge of the table, squinted her blue eyes shut, and clenched her teeth. "Not again! Can't you make him stop?"

She had voiced the question I couldn't articulate.

Jade Ann expressed my next question too. "What's wrong with that kid?"

"Nothing's wrong. Mattie isn't hurting anyone." Miss Mackenzie tapped her fingernail on the table. "Do your work, okay?"

Mattie left his chair, flapped his hands over his head, and cawed like a crow warning others of danger.

Miss Mackenzie followed him at a distance.

Mattie lodged himself back into his hiding spot between the wall and the bookcase, then banged his head against the cinder blocks.

Miss Mackenzie maneuvered herself behind him, and her arms restrained his hands. "I won't let you hurt yourself, Mattie. When you are safe, I will let go."

The dynamics of the special education classroom were too difficult to detach from, so I set my observation template aside. I kept an eye on Henry, watched the way Miss Mackenzie interacted with Mattie, and helped Jade Ann finish a math assignment. Mattie calmed down but never returned to the table, so Jade Ann and I colored until it was time for her to return to her regular classroom.

After dismissal, Miss Mackenzie invited me to sit with her in the reading nook. "Your visit didn't hurt Mattie, you know."

My throat tightened with each passing second, my words corralled by emotions. I shook my head.

"He's autistic and can't communicate easily. Maybe he thought we ignored him, or he felt bewildered. He could have been expressing excitement, even joy."

Mattie's screams left an indelible impression upon me, and on that October day, when I descended the school's wide steps, I no longer believed in myself. A special education teacher needed emotional strength to withstand such onslaughts, and my innermost self recognized its weakness.

I went on to earn a master's degree in special education, but I practiced the art of teaching in a regular classroom.

⁂

Dr. Holland settled back into his chair.

I considered gathering my belongings and running away from the situation, flicking his ear on the way out, but I didn't. For once, I controlled my impulse to escape evaluation and judgment. I needed his adult fingers to latch onto until my newly defined self found its equilibrium.

The doctor's damned voice interrupted a second time. "Do you know what Asperger syndrome is?"

Indeed. Mattie defined autism, but Brian, the student I loved and feared—that child linked to the events that had brought me to Dr. Holland in the first place—defined Asperger syndrome.

The horror that I might have inflicted the same kind of harm on others that Brian had inflicted upon me stopped me cold. I reacted as if the doctor had diagnosed leprosy; not a lick of common sense suggested I'd already survived a lifetime with this syndrome. I felt a kinship with the emperor who wore no clothes. The doctor had ripped off my mask, and I feared my nakedness.

Dr. Holland explained without condescension. "Autism is a developmental disorder that causes a person to have trouble communicating and interacting with others. It's called a spectrum disorder because there are many variations in the degree to which it affects different individuals. Because you have sophisticated language skills and a very high IQ, your type of autism is called Asperger syndrome."

It couldn't be. The two labels, autism and Asperger syndrome, were separate in my mind, as different as day and night. I watched as the color of the Prussian blue rug bled into the brown hardwood floor. Asperger syndrome was a type of autism?

I chided my inner self: *Shut up. I'm trying to listen.* This is why I've always felt different, set apart, unlikable. It's why I intuitively understood the difference between Brian's temper tantrums and meltdowns. The powerful need to integrate him with his neurotypical peers was the projection of a wish I'd made for myself when I was a fourth grader. Understanding the mechanics of his shunning came from personal experience.

Dr. Holland shifted in his chair and tried to catch my eye. "Are you aware you haven't looked at me since you came in?"

I understood the significance of his observation. Poor eye contact was a common characteristic of Asperger syndrome. Indeed, I avoided it at all costs, even with Joel, my children, and my friends. Eyes probed places more private than my body, confused truth with lies, and detected the absence of some part of my soul that should be present.

Dr. Holland's pompous bearing evaporated. His feet shifted to a comfortable position, his knees slightly parted, and he hunched forward. "Tell me how you played as a child."

"I was happy." This was where my therapists started; then, they spent months challenging the veracity of my words.

"Yes, but I want to know *how* you played."

I'd never been asked that question. "I liked to be alone and watch things." My response didn't begin to express the hyper-focused, delightful engrossment of observing a stagnant pool, day after day.

A sun-warmed board bridged the irrigation ditch's silver seam. I draped myself across it and wondered if the snails moving through the muck in slow-motioned hurry noticed the coolness of the shadows cast by water skippers. Did the black bugs know they were trapped where the water's edge met the sky?

I coaxed snails onto my finger and waited for them to feel safe enough to extend their tentacles. Often, they retracted one and looked at me with only one eye. I believed they saw half a world, so I closed an eye, too, hoping to see Earth their way.

The water skippers proved too mercurial to touch. Their inability to sink beneath the water or rise above it should have made them easy prey, but their aloof and unsociable habits proved a perfect foil to spending an afternoon trapped inside my collecting jar.

While I talked with the meadowlarks and grasshoppers in the pasture, I donned an imaginary spiral shell and slowly hurried across the silky dirt or spread my arms out to the side, skimming across the top of the tall grass like the water skippers skating on water.

I went nowhere fast, disconnected from the ordinary world, encased in an autistic glass shell.

⁂

Dr. Holland probed. "How did you make friends at school?"

"I didn't."

⁂

During first grade at Brimhall Elementary School in 1962, fall weather mellowed the playground. I sailed toward clouds on a swing, trying to touch their edges with my new shoes. I proudly nursed blisters raised by swinging on the monkey bars or jumped rope near the girls who sang rhymes. Most often, though, I watched the ants living at the playground's edge.

The popular girls' shadows darkened the cracked blacktop where I knelt near an ant nest. "What are you doing?" The voice belonged to the bold girl who sat behind me and often peeked her head over my shoulder to copy answers from my workbook.

I responded to their black silhouettes without looking up. "Watching ants."

The girls' shadows glided away, and their voices faded into the distance.

⁂

Before the hour ended, I had shared enough to confirm Dr. Holland's diagnosis. Even I couldn't deny the traits. I lived on the periphery of others' activity. My dolls had no names, I didn't open the gate to play with the little girl who lived on the other side of it, and I occupied a magical land watching bugs.

"My fee entitles you to another hour of my time." Dr. Holland rose. "You might find it helpful to talk more."

Physically stiff, emotionally numb, and spiritually sore, I rose from the couch and wiggled into my winter coat. I left his office and prayed to God in whom I did not believe: *protect me from me.* I didn't want to explore anything. I was fifty-eight years old, tired, and in so deep, I couldn't breathe.

This time, understanding a new label and accepting it as my new identity would happen on my terms.

I didn't want to delve into Asperger syndrome; I wanted to escape. Lithium held bipolar disorder at bay, and I used the skills Alice taught me to shield myself from borderline personality disorder, but nothing could stop the genetic flaw from manifesting itself. There was no hope of protecting myself from autism.

I did not want to be the moth battering herself against the light again. My wings had lost their silvery scales in past battles and were too fragile to open.

Schools should be magical places where bright holes are poked into the fabric of tomorrow—where questions are more important than answers, ideas than profits—a noisy, messy, exciting, now-place where children can find their own place in the universe and become whole, and so holy, while sitting in the sun with their teachers watching ants.
—Arden Georgi Thompson

Lights Off, Door Closed

On the way home from Dr. Holland's office, I decided to lie to Joel about what I had learned. The sound from the table saw drowned out the noise of the back door opening and closing behind me as I entered our home. Once inside the kitchen, I slipped my evaluation into an oversized cookbook that hadn't been used since the 60s.

The scent of woodchips accompanied Joel's footsteps into the kitchen. "How'd your appointment go?"

"Fine."

That's how much I allowed Joel to know about my life-altering experience. My intent wasn't to deceive. I needed to process the diagnosis that, from then on, would separate our lives into before and after. I believed a normal person had perished several hours earlier, and I found no words to inform my husband of her death.

The following day, as I listened from the comfort of my bed to Joel making his breakfast, my evaluation became the tell-tale heart, beating inside its hiding place, audible in our upstairs bedroom. I waited to hear Joel's truck leave before giving in to the need to check that it was still concealed.

Outside, the birds puffed their feathers against the cold. I sat at my old oak table in my outdated farmhouse kitchen and stewed. My normally short attention span fixated on dredging up memories of when I might have behaved like Brian. I didn't scream every day, but I couldn't pinpoint what I did that was indicative of autism.

The heartbeat grew louder. I went downstairs. The warped cover of *Betty Crocker's New Boys and Girls Cookbook* opened easily, and I lifted the secret in my hand. I took it and a hot cup of coffee to the table and carefully read the evaluation three times. Then, I stuffed it as deeply into the trash as I could and dumped coffee grounds over it.

The Christmas tree became part of the background, my shopping list an annoyance, and I didn't feel like baking gingerbread cookies anymore. I resolved to shake off the uncomfortable diagnosis, but its shadow accompanied me wherever I went and whatever I did.

Rage at the mental health system roiled inside me. In 1985, on my first wedding anniversary, I'd admitted to myself I acted like my mother—draping across furniture like discarded clothing. I was thirty years old when I first reached out for help with depression.

Through the decades, I'd accrued a host of diagnoses. According to the professionals, I had post-traumatic stress disorder, major depressive disorder, obsessive compulsive disorder, social anxiety disorder, generalized anxiety disorder, panic disorder, dissociative disorder, and seasonal affective disorder, and I was told I malingered. Loved that one.

Being on the spectrum was at the root of all of it. Dr. Larsen had lumped all my problematic behavior into one umbrella diagnosis when he suggested I had borderline personality disorder. He never probed for an underlying condition.

Each day since Dr. Larsen had prescribed it, I'd swallowed lithium and prayed to God in whom I did not believe to grant me stability. Each night the medication, in some undefinable and imperceptible way, bestowed immunity from mania, the bane of my existence. But there'd be no similar relief from autism. There was no medication for that.

⌒

At school, another Christmas vacation neared. Tension at the alternative school was high. These were the students who had intimidated the bus driver in September. The student body, sixteen youths from ages fourteen through eighteen, had all been expelled from the middle school or high school. They handled their problems with violence or extreme withdrawal, effectively separating them from their regular schools.

They battled learning disabilities, substance abuse, domestic violence, poverty, homelessness, and neglect. Some were mentally ill. Most were involved with the juvenile justice system. I considered them survivors of the highest degree. Like Jesse, their ebullient natures and uncompromising protective strategies left me in awe.

However, I identified most with the hider. One girl hadn't uttered a word since she was in elementary school. She hid under the social worker's desk whenever she could and drew beautiful wings using a collection of abandoned pens. A sixth sense moved herself away from people.

The special education teacher who believed in children, Cam, was expecting a new baby. So was Trevor, the oldest student who juggled a job, meeting with his parole officer, alcoholism, a misbehaving pickup truck, and classroom expectations. They both kept ultrasound pictures taped to their desks.

Several days before vacation, Trevor stood outside my door. "Ms. D., I need help with something."

This from a student who spun his tires and dropped the F-bomb with equal frequency. "What's up, Trev?"

"Would you help me throw a party for Mr. C?"

"Do you mean a baby shower?"

He did.

We conferred. Trevor would spread the word to the other students. The jobs of putting up streamers and balloons and buying the cake became mine.

Later in the day, Cam slipped into my room. "I've been thinking about throwing a surprise shower for Trevor. What do you think?"

"I think it's a great idea! How about I get the streamers and cake." Inside I melted. Signs of love at the alternative school, and I was smack dab in the middle of them.

On the last day before Christmas break, I arrived early and set up several cafeteria tables in a far corner of the gym. Garlands of twisted blue and pink crepe paper with matching balloons staged the area for the cake and gifts.

By the end of the day, both fathers shuttled binkies, blankets, diapers, and toys to their vehicles. The last I saw of them, Cam had his hand on Trevor's shoulder.

What more of a Christmas gift could I have wished for?

☙

In January, we all waited. Cam's day came first. He had a son. Trevor's baby arrived in March, a little girl who instantly became a reason to turn his life around. He resolved to stop smoking and swearing.

☙

That year, on the last Wednesday of the school year, the June weather was so hot and humid the flag hugged the pole. I arrived after the morning bell and found Torey's truck already in the parking lot. Glad to know she was in the building, I headed for the office to say a quick hello before setting to work at my desk.

A crisis was unfolding, but I hadn't noticed the tension. Torey spoke to me when I entered the office. "Beth, I'm glad you're here. Go tell Cam and Steve to keep the kiddos in their rooms. Don't make a big deal of it."

As I walked down the hall toward the classrooms, I noticed the social worker sitting on the floor near her desk. She wasn't the sort I'd expect to do that.

Cam and Steve gave me a thumbs-up. I left the academic wing and headed back to the stairs that abutted the double doors of the rear entry.

An ambulance backed in.

I hurried to the office. Torey and I watched the paramedics grab their equipment. They entered the social worker's office. A male voice assured someone they'd be okay. A case snapped open, then closed.

The paramedics brought a gurney to the room. I heard the sigh and knew someone's weight had settled on it. The belts snapped into place. I remembered the feeling of being robbed of choice.

Through the tall window, Torey and I watched as the gurney was locked into the back of the ambulance. I saw her face. It was the silent girl, the one who hid under desks.

The ambulance's doors closed, and the lights rolled across the playground. Slowly, it moved toward the road.

I laid my hand on the sun-warmed glass and sent the girl a silent benediction. "You are brave enough."

That was the moment I heard the double meaning. Would she think I meant she was brave enough to die? Or live? I hadn't been specific.

I left my hand where it was and turned to Torey. "There isn't any help, is there?

Torey shook her head. "We can only care, Beth."

No small feat, caring. Schools tried to stop hemorrhages with Band-aids.

I expected the moment I turned off the lights in my classroom for the last time to be dramatic, but it was anticlimactic. No one in the bustling school noticed but me. In the hall, Cam and Steve talked about their plans for the next year. I recognized the intensity of their reflections. They were sorting out what had worked and what didn't. New ideas would grow during July and August as they planned different strategies for a new beginning in September.

I listened to them speak of things they hadn't finished and what they'd change. They lit up like fireflies.

And then, I heard it: the true ending of the school year. Cam and Steve left their dream-weaving to work on their cumulative folders. The repetition of this tired tradition brought me comfort, and I laughed at their frustration with the process.

"I don't know why we have to do this; it's all on the computer."

"Let's not do it then."

Their daring to defy authority astounded me. I had just witnessed the passing of the torch. It was time for me to say goodbye to June.

"Lights out, door closed," I'd say whenever my class vacated the classroom. The lights were out.

All I needed to do was close the door.

Shadows keep me company. Now one before by streetlamp cast,
a dark exaggeration boldly strides, while to my right a moon-born
waif climbs warily beside. Each from, and yet not of me, they'll
walk into my day though others cannot see, for if I define
my shadows, they, too, define and sometimes limit me.
—Arden Georgi Thompson

The Ants' Nest

In September, the time of new beginnings, I told Joel I was on the spectrum.

He told me it was fine, and, again, we didn't explore the subject. He probably meant it, but I didn't trust the vague word *fine*, and deep in my heart, I doubted him. How could he not see ugliness too?

On a light-hearted kind of day, I tried to talk with him. "What I really want to know is how to chat. I get that I'm supposed to ask someone how they are, but everyone says they're fine, which is always a freakin' lie. Or people tell me about the weather, as if I don't know it's raining. Or they mention the traffic, like there are cars—wait for it—on the road."

Joel was making pizza. He looked up from the cutting board; the smell of sweet onions filled the space between us. "What are you doing?"

I shared my thoughts about that particular phrase with him for the first time. "There it is, that question. I hate it! What am I doing?" My hands panned the horizon. "Let's imagine all the possibilities, and you pick one!"

"They said it might rain tomorrow."

"So what. I want to try to chat."

"Me too." Joel sighed, set down the knife, and brushed a few stray onion bits into the trash. "Just say something connected, like the grass will need to get cut or something. Make it up if you have to."

"Why would I make it up?"

"That's chatting. You just say stuff."

I collapsed onto a kitchen chair. "But why do that when you can talk about something important?"

"Because most people don't make lesson plans, Beth; they just open their mouths and say *stuff*."

In the fall, I began researching autism in earnest. Like millions of other neurodivergent women, I was part of the Lost Generation (those who grew up before pediatricians and schools began specifically screening for autism). I entered into therapy as an adult in the late eighties. It wasn't until 1994 that Asperger syndrome, the name given to high-functioning autism prior to 2013, appeared in the *Diagnostic and Statistical Manual of Mental Disorders*.

Of course I was missed; no one was looking.

On the pages of books and on the internet, I found others like me. Shy. Odd. Smart. Bullied. Naive. Unconventional. Clumsy. Honest. Curious. Rigid. Quirky. I shared traits making me a fellow member of a tribe. No longer alone in the company of others, the feeling of inclusion quieted one of the voices inside my head that cried. Instead of being dismissed with an oh-that-happens-to-everyone platitude, I knew someone, somewhere, understood what it was like to grow up differently than their peers in the same way I had.

The work of Dr. Nouchine Hadjikhani explained the deep discomfort I felt when I looked into someone's eyes. Through the analysis of brain scans, she discovered that a specific part of the brain dedicated to a baby's natural attraction to faces was activated by eye contact. That part of the brain, the subcortical system, was overactive in people with autism, and its overstimulation caused anxiety. This was the reason I never looked anyone in the eye, not because of dishonesty, being unconcerned, or embarrassment like I'd been accused.

In the 1980s, Simon Baron-Cohen and his colleagues developed a *theory of mind* model of autism, which attributed autism to *mindblindness*, an inability to understand what other people knew, wanted, felt, or believed. This premise informed my conceptualization of autism. It was abhorrent to me.

A new theory, postulated in 2007 by neuroscientists Henry Markram, Kamila Markram, and Tania Rinaldi, posited that hyper-perception, hyper-attention, hyper-memory, and hyper-emotionality underlie autism.[6] This theory aligned with my experience.

The *Intense World Syndrome* suggested a hyperfunctional autistic brain was overwhelmed by what were ordinary stimuli for a neurotypical brain. What might a person do with an overload of information, intense emotions, and an overactive memory? I withdrew from everything unpredictable, especially people such as sociable and outgoing Mrs. Westcott.

Patterns and systematics allowed me to navigate chaos. My strategy to handle social conundrums was to pick a friend I admired and mimic him or her. I came to realize others didn't shun me; rather, I avoided people at all costs. And that avoidance created a feedback loop. I didn't engage; therefore I couldn't, so I didn't until loneliness added up to isolation. I didn't withdraw from people so they wouldn't hurt me first but to shield myself from too much input and uncertainty.

From preschool to high school to the university to a classroom of my own, school provided structure, predictability, and a tolerable social environment. When I was young, my teachers were kinder than my parents, and during adolescence, they were mentors. In a

---

6. Markram, H., Rinaldi, T., & Markram, K. (2007, October 15). *The intense world syndrome—an alternative hypothesis for autism.* Frontiers in neuroscience. https://www.ncbi.nlm.nih.gov/pmc/articles/PMC2518049/.

way, I entered the school system's routine at age four and never left it. The loss of my career devastated me. School was my safe harbor, a home away from home. I lost the people, the place, and the things I loved—and needed.

As time wore on and my understanding grew. Acknowledging the fact that Asperger syndrome was a form of autism presented a hurdle. The spectrum of neurodivergence was just like the neurotypical spectrum—we all differ. It turned out that I had to accept that having autism was a lot like—well—a lot like being me before bipolar disorder pushed me underwater.

Should I have been a teacher? No doubt about it. I wasn't always ill. I'd been nominated by my peers for Teacher of the Year three times. That happened for a reason. Autism was a barrier between me and the evaluation process, so I never entered the competition. The true test, though, was the number of former students who told me I'd changed their lives for the better. I had excelled in my profession.

Once I became more comfortable, I made a grave mistake. I told family members I was on the spectrum and requested that they understand my reticence to join them in social situations. I thought they'd change their minds about why I preferred to be left out of everyday chatter. My brain was wired differently. My request wasn't grounded in snobbery or dislike.

Instead, they treated me like a child.

Working around my idiosyncrasies was ordinary to my son and daughter. They'd accommodated me their entire lives. Joel's mother and sister? Not so much. I assumed Joel understood my differences, but he hadn't scoured the internet as I had. He didn't have a lifetime of experiences to bolster his conceptualizations. In all likelihood, stereotypes informed his opinions. Joel cared and respected my needs, but he couldn't explain or advocate for me. I expected support he didn't know how to give.

✑

A year later, in August, Joel's sister asked me what I wanted for my birthday.

I exploded. "Nothing. Why can't you wrap your thick skull around that? N-O-T-H-I-N-G. I want to go out for ice cream with Joel. No cards, no phone calls, no stupid presents. I want everyone to leave me alone." I hit her with all of my pent up frustration.

I meant it. My birthday was supposed to be mine. Mine. I was sixty years old and believed it was *my* turn to have the day go *my* way once. I'd stated my case when Joel and I were first married and reiterated it to his family each August thereafter: I only wanted to be with my husband. I wasn't playing head games; nor was I being coy. I'd stated the literal honest truth, then eaten cake and thanked people for calling and opened surprises because it was polite to do so.

I should have kept my mouth shut.

On the day of my birthday, Joel's sister brought a little cake, a card, and a little present to the house. "Don't worry; I didn't do much."

She patted me on the shoulder, then skirted past into my kitchen.

I smiled, said thank you, and wished for cat claws to draw blood.

✑

Months passed, summer stretched into September, and then to a mild and pleasant autumn. Joel started walking on eggshell flooring. I lived as if anything I said would hang like flypaper from the ceiling. We withdrew again into separate lives lived in physical proximity. I remained convinced happiness was the bane of my existence and evicted it at all cost. Thinking that choice to be protective, I didn't have the wisdom to understand that protecting my marriage was destroying it.

Our home grew brittle and quiet. Neither of us was in the wrong; the gulf was simply too wide to cross. We didn't communicate, and we both made inaccurate assumptions. There had been a lot of damage done to our relationship, and the cumulative effect broke it.

Another Halloween neared. I heard shuffling upstairs. Thinking I'd help, I entered the bedroom. The fire-safe box was open, and Joel sorted old tax returns and other documents into piles.

"Why don't you do that when it's tax time?"

"This makes it easier."

Before Thanksgiving, I laid on the bed while Joel sorted through the clothes in his closet. "Why don't you wait until you open your Christmas presents to see what you get first?"

"I know what I want to keep."

Weeks before Christmas, while I was drinking coffee and watching the morning news, a vehicle pulled into the driveway. I watched a stranger take the table saw. Panicked, I met Joel at the door. "What are you doing?"

"I don't want it anymore."

I knew, of course, I knew. This time, Joel would never come back.

While Joel emptied the house, contacted a realtor, and searched for an apartment, I hid in the guest bedroom, focused on how best to end my life. Alternatives didn't exist. I smashed things I loved, and Joel took the detritus to the dump.

I stopped taking lithium.

Part of putting my affairs in order included talking with my friends.

Kathleen's house smelled like Christmas when she opened her door. "So, you made me promise I'd just listen and not try to talk you out of anything." She hugged me, then held me at arm's length. "That's pretty hard to do, you know."

I'd practiced what I wanted to say, but the words sounded stupid when I replayed them in my mind. Instead, I asked about her trip to California.

The shift happened during a pause. It was my turn to talk.

Kathleen seemed to fold up; she leaned away and held her mug in both hands, tipping her head downward to take a sip.

I pulled a lap blanket over my shoulders to hide beneath its folds. "The first day I knew for certain he was leaving, I drove into town and tried to buy heroin."

Kathleen was appalled. Her eyes widened, and she cinched her eyebrows. "You did *what*?"

"Yup. I had a perfect plan, except for finding the stuff." I let the blanket fall to my lap. "Imagine a gray-haired teacher in a beat-up truck pulling over to the curb saying, 'Excuse me, do you have any heroin for sale?'" I paused for effect. "I was very polite, but no one had a clue where I might find some."

As I elaborated, we laughed, the situation evoking memories of middle schoolers' awkward moments of being innocent while being accused of a wrong—or of being guilty and denying it with aplomb.

I went into Kathleen's kitchen to get a couple of cookies and resettled. "It gets better. Since there wasn't a chance in hell I'd find heroin on the street, the next day, I figured out how to navigate the dark web and bought some fentanyl from a company in Ukraine." My eyes glanced at a tree outside the window. "They sent a tracking number. First, the package went to Charles de Gaulle airport in France."

"You could see that?"

"Yup, just like you can watch an Amazon package. Then, it went to New York, and from there to Bangor, and that's when the DEA got involved."

"You're an idiot."

"You have no idea."

"How in the world could you be so stupid?" Her eyebrow arched, and she leaned away from me. "Are you going to get arrested?" Her voice slid up an octave.

"I don't think so; I've been watching and waiting for blue lights and men in black suits, but I think the whole thing was a scam, even the email from the DEA." I was annoyed she didn't understand the obvious reason I put myself in jeopardy. "I wasn't planning on cleaning up the mess, Kathleen. I didn't care."

She pulled her feet under her and looked away. "I feel guilty." Her toes curled inside her socks. "I knew you weren't okay, but I didn't call. I went to California and had a great time." My friend rose to grab tissues. "I should have done something."

My eyes welled with tears. "There was nothing you could have or should have done; I really need you to get that. My decision belongs to me; it's private. I'm tired of fighting my brain. For you to consider suicide would take some unfathomable, horrific despair. From my perspective, it's gentle and quiet. That's the distinction. I don't want to die; I want to stop hurting. People beg for morphine when they are in pain, you know. I've hurt for a long time."

A snap of anger straightened her back; she rose from her rocking chair. "You're telling me I'm not enough; your friends aren't enough to live for! That makes me so angry."

I stood up too. "It's not fair for you to say I don't value our friendship. I'm not playing with a balance. You're always important, but Joel's my life, and I need him, and he's gone."

I was surprised by my anger. "That's not it, though." I sat back down and looked at my distraught friend. "I want to walk away from me, too, but there's no escaping. I keep showing up no matter what I do or where I go."

Kathleen laughed. "How do you do that? You always make me laugh when things are terrible." She sat down beside me.

I reached to grasp my friend's hands. "Trust me, Kathleen, you have to trust me to make the right decision. It's just as selfish of you to think I should be in pain to keep you from feeling bad. Think of it this way; if I had cancer, I might choose to stop chemo. You'd be sad and cry, but you wouldn't be appalled by my decision. You might even sit with me as I slipped away. I might be killed in a car accident tomorrow; you'd mourn but wouldn't feel guilty.

"I don't think this is any different. I'm tired, and the pain is the same kind I feel every day. Whatever it is, nothing has ever taken the edge off or made it go away. I'm not wrong. You just can't see my invisible wounds."

My friend's hand trembled. "But talk to someone!"

"I've tried. I've been talking about this since we started teaching thirty years ago. You know I've been to a lot of therapists. I'm not willing to try any more. I'm tired, that's all there is to it."

My doppelgänger paid for my cremation and bought a gun.

Like a moth forgetting earthly things while pursuing the beauty of a distant star, can we be and yet not know who or what we are?
—Arden Georgi Thompson

The Cocoon

Inside her cocoon's woven knot, the caterpillar's body protected her imaginal discs, specialized islands of tissues that had organized while she was inside her egg: one set for eyes, shoulders, and legs, and a neural knot for a brain. During her time of change, enzymes digested the rest of her body. Her beleaguered brain retained its memories.

Fluid remains, disintegrated caterpillar soup, swirled. Some molecules, those pushed farthest away from the core, organized into veined rinds constrained by the cocoon's protective tangled threads.

When it was time, the cocoon split open, and the caterpillar exited her protective cloak. She pumped crystal-clear insect blood into the rind's veins. Droplets of waste shed like dripping tears, leaving the caterpillar vulnerable until the rinds dried and hardened into scabs covered in delicate silver scales.

Then, the disfigured caterpillar rose into the bottom of the sky, beautiful to behold.

~

The real cocoon was macabre.

On the eve of my thirty-fourth wedding anniversary, I entered the woods with a garnet-hued, thirty-five-liter backpack stuffed with everything I needed to end things once and for all.

On that day, the expansive sky wore fine gauze to stay warm. An area near a small brook, clear of thorned blackberry brambles and poison ivy, attracted me. I thought it a nice spot, a nondescript description of an unremarkable place.

Foremost on my mind was protecting others from my violence. To that end, I chose to hide inside a survival bivvy, a cylindrical Mylar bag that I'd sewn shut so it wouldn't leak.

Once I had suspended the bivvy between two spruce trees and spiked the corners, the small tent appeared to be a giant's discarded caramel wrapper, more like a slumped hammock than the pup tent it was meant to be. I stepped back to admire my work. Joel would be proud of my knots but damned disappointed with the sagging walls.

One swipe of my utility knife opened a four-foot horizontal lop-sided grin under the tent's ridgeline. This entry point, higher than my waist, hiccupped an unexpected impediment into my plan.

How was I going to get in?

I shook my head at my lack of foresight. True to form, I'd fucked up already.

Making a vertical cut to climb inside would defeat the purpose of creating a container to hide my body. With the knife safely stowed in my pack's zippered pouch, I set my gear out of harm's way so I wouldn't trip over it and scatter the contents to the four winds.

At first, treating the lower edge of the grin as if it were a piece of barbed wire I could step over seemed logical. I pressed down, but it neither stretched nor ripped.

Hanging onto a nearby sapling, I grabbed the left hem of my jeans. Using the fabric as a sling, I lifted my leg and dropped my boot-clad foot inside, a move that shifted me into the position of straddling a Mylar-thin boy's bike with no handlebars.

For balance, I tugged at an overhead branch as if it were a subway strap. My inner ballerina arched her back, and I raised my right leg in a pathetic bent-knee arabesque and pulled myself over the lip into the confines of the bivvy.

Just before my right boot made contact with solid ground, I caught a glimpse of garnet—my forgotten pack. All my necessaries were out of reach.

I shrugged off my coat and spread it like a mat as I studied the problem. How could I retrieve my pack without further damaging my death chamber? I'd already poked holes in the floor.

The tent's ceiling foiled my attempt to stand upright, so I dipped out of the crooked grin and pulled myself to full height, which strained the parachute cord.

My knots held.

The sloped vertical wall, thin as a balloon but as stalwart as a castle's crenelated top, remained an unbreachable barrier.

The trunk of the tree I used for balance on the way in was out of reach. I chose to execute a trust fall to grab it, which worked. My feet remained inside, and I, a leaning plank, remained stuck, albeit in a different position.

Gripping the rough bark as tightly as I could, I craned my neck to assess my position, a movement that flipped my body and ripped my hands across the tree bark. I fell like a goldfish sliding over the lip of its bowl onto broken branches, rocks, and the duff of the forest floor, damned near killing myself.

To fuck and back! Palms skinned and bleeding, lungs fighting my rib cage to breathe, and embarrassed as all hell, I hunkered down until the pain eased. Anger helped me rise and heave my backpack into my improvised coffin.

I repeated the sequence of pulling my feet up and over the sagging lip for the last time.

Shit! I thought there'd be more room, but there was barely enough for me, my pack, and God in whom I did not believe.

The hair-rippingly frustrating experience of getting everything into the shelter finished, I set the stand I'd built in place, rigged the revolver into position, then secured it all with scarlet ribbons to control the recoil.

I twisted to maneuver my head under the gun onto my pillow, a stuffed rabbit Joel had given me when I first started working with a therapist three decades ago. I reflected on the comedy of errors while setting up my cocoon and laughed at the absurdity of my predicament.

The light that filtered through the trees painted an ever-changing pattern on silvery Mylar walls. I drifted in and out of here-and-there and now-and-then pleats of time during the afternoon hours. I read aloud to the chipmunk chattering in a hidden spot across the brook whenever my attention could grab hold of the words from Mary Norton's book, *The Borrowers*: "The floor of the sitting room was carpeted with deep red blotting paper, which was warm and cozy, and soaked up the spills."

After having spent most of my life looking down, the grinning slit forced me to look up. I traced the edge of the sky, imagining it as icing spread around each spruce needle, flowing into the trunk's nooks and crannies, dripping into the space between the dust and sand grains below.

Light played with the rippled Mylar, imitating the irrigation ditch's still surface. Inside, the memory of lying on the sun-warmed board comforted my still heart, but my brain was too busy to notice.

I talked with Joel in my mind. I imagined his refusal to join me in my little room and heard him tell me again that I was the only one who could figure things out. I had come to realize just how alone I was in this; he wouldn't enter into a pushmepullyou conversation. Life pushed for ascendance; death pulled me into mystery.

Joel. Absent. Silent. Don't do it for me, he'd said when he left me at the hospital. He was right. Today was my day. Peaceful. Final. I'd do it for me. It's okay, I said to me, myself, and I; we'll be alone together.

In my imaginings, I chased the sky's bottom edge to the pounding surf where the moon's pull danced with Earth's gravity, commingling air and water into a lacy fringe. Blue whales carried sky bubbles in their lungs deep below the sea's surface.

I exhaled, slid the bunny against my chest to hold my heart instead of pillowing my head, then reached for the gun steadied by the stand. My exploring finger traced the trigger. It entered the guard, tensed, relaxed, and repositioned itself. Muscles squeezed until metal grated against metal, moving the cylinder an infinitesimal but perceivable distance.

Even the wind held its breath.

The grin's sleepy mouth sagged open as my emotions flat-lined. Earth rolled away from day, and that quick change to dusk happened, turning the sky above me to a faint duck-egg blue. My muscles unlatched their bond to bone, making my limbs feel rubbery. My mind, trapped between the platform and the revolver's tip, shifted its concentration from my last thoughts to mystery.

What would happen next?

I followed the sky deeper and watched it in my mind's eye as it sifted down through the dirt, caressing tree roots until it filled Earth's hollows. Caves were places where pieces of the sky settled of their own accord, but visible light, something without substance, was denied access. Odd. Light could flow through liquid water or solid ice, but the sky was forbidden entry.

I watched silvery ribbons slide across the bivvy's surface and bade myself goodbye in the reverse way of a new mother welcoming her child. I'd read my last story, taken my last step, and now would lose my last tooth and take my last breath.

The rocks and branches beneath my body no longer hurt, and my angel knelt outside the tent.

Know this; darkness is not real.

I slipped out of my body and was bound by the Mylar wrapping, similar to my experience in the hospital but not as expansive and more stable.

Light is all around you.

A snail that seemed too real to be imaginary, but too imaginary to be real, inched its way across my finger, which lay near my cheek. It sat quietly enough for me to reassure it that it was safe to emerge from its fright. When the snail rotated one tentacle, I looked it in the eye and assured it I was brave enough to explore half the world at a time too.

Light is all there is.

I stared into the snail's eye for a long time. Its gaze glided through my cornea, dove past the muscles that pulled my blue iris closed, and swam through the vitreous humor. It smoothed my retina as if running its hand across a wrinkled blanket on a bed.

The snail spoke to me as if it were the angel. "Don't you understand? Remember, you have to use your heart to find love, not your eyes or your hands. Joel lives within you and you within him. Love still *is*. Stop looking for it!"

Light is love.

Up turned into down. I was back in the pasture gazing into the irrigation ditch, and I could stay for as long as I wanted by hovering in an in-between state of mind that was as palpable as it was amorphous.

I realized I had the rest of my life to think things over.

Light is all around you. Light all there is. Light is love.
$E=mc^2$

Within the cocoon, a surprise, more precious than gold and lithium combined, unfurled in a four-part sequence.[7]

The Surprise
Phase One
Freeze

An incongruity captured my attention: I felt happy.

According to research, this flick, called the freeze phase, lasted 1/25th of a second. During that minuscule moment, my brain ripped the rug out from under me. It stopped thinking.

Electroencephalography could have measured the jolt. Had a specific array of electrodes been attached to my scalp, it would have recorded a spike of biochemical activity within my brain in a pattern called the P300 wave.

The shock, a bit like pushing a rocket that had already lifted a foot off the launchpad back into position, robbed my face of all expression. After all, I'd stop thinking.

The Surprise
Phase Two
Find

After screeching to a halt long before the first second had finished its tick, my brain sucked in enough cerebral air to free dive and explore for as long as needed. Rebooted thoughts reached into every nook and cranny, running their hands across every neural edge. Gray matter analyzed information at a drop rate that eclipsed the partnership of a snail-paced computer processor and Google's turtle-like ability to peek through digital gates.

---

7. Luna, Tania, and LeeAnn Renninger. *Surprise: Embrace the Unpredictable, Engineer the Unexpected.* Perigee Trade, 2015.

My brain's free dive into deep inner space, a living cave filled with dendritic stalactites and stalagmites coated with neuro-transmitter snottite goo,[8] ended before the first half-second had a chance for the tick to reach toward the tock. In the same instantaneous way a person discovers the *snake* to be a stick; I resolved I was *safe*.

The Surprise
Phase Three
Shift

The find phase's resolution wasn't that I decided to live, pack up, and go home.

No.

I had entered that captivating glass marble of wonder, where I talked with the meadowlarks and caught grasshoppers in the pasture; the place where I had donned a spiral shell and slowly hurried across the silky dirt and spread my arms out to the side, skimming across the top of the tall grass like the water skippers.

I was in the place where thoughts traveled at the speed of light, disconnected from reality, trailing their fingers through Prussian blue.

Fucking Yoga Girl's ghost, still young, earnest, and lithe, got in the first word. "I see you found your happy place."

Alice laughed with delight. "Not paying much attention to your falling-apart world, now, are you?"

---

8. You didn't think you were going to read clean through my book without a reference to microbes, did you? Ecosystems exist in a myriad variety; some, devoid of sunlight, are powered by a chemical called hydrogen sulfide, the stinky gas that leaks from rotten eggs. One of these ecosystems is a microbial mat that coats the surface of some caves. Wee beasties secrete a sugar-based slime just as the epithelial cells that line your nose make that wonderful snotty stuff. Vast populations of creatures live inside the sea they generate for themselves. More living individuals than the number of human beings that have *ever* lived on Earth live within the amount of snot you'd sneeze into one tissue.

Dr. Holland, devoid of his Edwardian suit but still wearing rose-tinted round glasses, sat naked on his tufted leather throne. "Do you want to explore what that means?"

Derek watched from the sidelines and swirled cognac. Then, he laid down on the sun-warmed board next to me and searched through the muck with his fingers. He plucked a spiral shell filled with a sentient being from the mud and let the snail sit on his finger, knowing it, too, used patterns of thinking inside its tiny brain.

I noticed an oddity. Strange, we, two grown adults, fit on a board no wider than the span of my foot. I looked at Derek. "Makes you think, doesn't it?"

The Surprise
Phase Four
Sharing

Snap!

My surprise couldn't shut its mouth; it needed to spill what it had found as quickly as possible. What just happened? Did you see that? Derek and Alice were here! Or was it just me?

Outside, the blackness sifted apart from the duck-egg blue sky and fell. The gloaming turned green spruce tips gray, and the other-worldliness of the cocoon turned ordinary.

The air was cold and still.

I bolted upright, stopped short by the platform and the gun which snagged my neck like a fishing lure caught on a rock. I lifted the gun like a hiker might push a branch out of the way but couldn't continue to hold it up because I needed to roll that shoulder out from under the stand. The loaded and cocked pendulum fell each time I lifted it as I tried to create enough space to roll out from under.

Shit. I pictured myself on a gurney in an ambulance, shot in the shoulder like Matt Dillon on *Gunsmoke*.

As stuck as when I first tried to enter the cocoon through the grin, I maneuvered my head out of my contraption, which entailed solving the two-nail pub puzzle.[9]

Geez, Louise. Thank God Smith & Wesson hired excellent machinists to make parts. Nothing exploded.

Once free, the stuffed rabbit took a tumble. One of its black plastic eyes locked onto mine, and we broke into laughter, two giggly girls in a tent who had stayed up way too late. During one spasm, I peed my pants, which brought the surprise sequence to a close.

Chilled, I sidled crab-wise to the edge of the Mylar wall and pondered how to move my coat out from under me as it was covered by my gear which had scattered to the four corners of my small world. My hip hurt from lying atop the branch I had decided not to move earlier. I reassured myself everything was fine, yet I worried about the horror of having a dark wet patch on my coat, even though there was no one to see. The urine didn't penetrate the fabric, so I slipped my coat on while lying on my back.

Even inside the protective cocoon, I needed to cover the shame of my body.

Emergence began when I hurled one garnet-hued backpack containing the mess that had covered the Mylar floor out through the grin.

Again, I had moved the utility knife out of reach. Shit. How was I going to get out? With no need to keep the bivvy watertight so no blood would leak, I clambered through the opening unconcerned about tearing it from its lashings or ripping the grinning entry's wound wider.

My knots held until I pulled on the correct end of the parachute cord, unlashing the mess from the spruce trees.

---

9. *I knew you'd need to know:* The puzzle consists of two identical nails bent into a shape rather like the letter *d*, twisted together. Their entanglement is such that it seems as if the nails should slide apart easily, which they will. But it wouldn't be a classic puzzle if the feat were easy; there's a twist to it.

I felt unmitigated pride. Joel had spent years trying to teach me how to tie knots to no avail. Finally, I had succeeded.

Like any tent that comes out of its factory-packed stuff bag, the bivvy didn't fit into my pack, so I rolled it up, shouldered my backpack, and carried the second version of the cobra out of the woods, remembering to cross the stream the way I did when I first entered.

En pointe.

If you see things bright, clear-cut and new like after rain, or when
there's no mote to obscure the view, don't hide. It doesn't mean anything
is wrong with you, only that you've been entrusted with a gift.
—Arden Georgi Thompson

In This, I Trust

G ood moods don't last.

On my sixty-fourth birthday, I acted like an angry mother dragging a recalcitrant child to a time-out chair, marching myself off to the woods again. This time, my despair had nothing to do with Joel. I was sick and tired of feeling suicidal, a thought process as reflexive and unavoidable as a sneeze. The choice was clear—pull the damn trigger or call for help. Neither alternative appealed to me.

I settled into a shallow depression near a leaning beech tree, dialed 911, and disclosed my circumstances. The barrel of the revolver, cold against my upper ear, affirmed that the choice to live or die remained under my control.

An indescribable fear of death, deep and cold in my underbelly, made my muscles shake. What if I wasn't waiting for me on the other side?

I called Joel.

Our conversation evaporated from my memory as soon as each word was uttered. I said my goodbyes and hoped my assurances of how much I loved him stayed in his heart forever.

He hesitated, probably searching for something to say.

I took his hesitation to mean he refused to engage in what he took to be a game.

Again and again, like the pounding surf, the resolve to shoot myself swelled, then ebbed away, only to swell again. Then, my fear made the decision. I'd live to fight; that was the preordained purpose of this showdown. I wasn't Chief Joseph and couldn't exist in a perpetual stalemate any longer.

A helicopter appeared so low overhead I could see dings in the landing skids. The downdraft from the blades shook the canopy branches, and the bubble of Plexiglas shielding the pilot reminded me of a ferocious dragonfly scudding over garden greenery scouting for prey.

I thought of waving like a subdued survivor on a desert island but instead sat up and returned my belongings to my backpack. Pictures from my wedding and of my children. My gun and stuffed bunny. The helicopter gained height and flew into the distance.

Alone, I walked out of the woods.

When I reached my car, I searched my pack for my car keys. I peered through the driver's side window, thinking I'd left them in the ignition, and watched the reflection of a pair of black boots approach. I laid my head against the hot glass and waited.

"What are you doing, ma'am?"

"Looking for my keys." I moved to the rear window and shielded my eyes with my hand to look inside. "I really need them."

"You wouldn't happen to have a gun, would you?"

Three other officers clad in body armor with assault rifles at the ready, neared.

Amused rather than alarmed, I turned to face them. Imagine all that fuss. "Seriously? A bit of overkill, don't you think?"

No one laughed.

I supposed they were right; a dysregulated old woman had the potential to be dangerous. Only I knew I posed no threat. My weapon was secured in the trunk of a cruiser, passing out of my hands forever. The officer placed me on a psych hold and stated I'd be free to go once a doctor cleared me.

A white ambulance arrived on the scene.

There was no streetlamp to talk with, my angel was absent, and the ride to the hospital was nearly silent.

⁂

After three days in the emergency room, a bed opened on the Behavioral Health ward. Due to disruptions caused by COVID-19, it wasn't until the fifth day that I met with the attending psychiatrist, Dr. Schwartz.

After the necessary small talk, the doctor confronted me. "I see you've refused antidepressants. The physician assistant who prescribed them is very competent. They would have helped."

"If they helped, I wouldn't be here."

I explained to Dr. Schwartz that I wasn't depressed; I was sad and angry. I told him it was possible to stab your brain with pills, something I wasn't willing to do again. "I can't read anymore. Do you have any idea what that is like? Granted, it's not a life-threatening injury, but what if I try new meds and lose a different part of my brain?"

The doctor leaned toward me, listened, and, unlike Dr. Larsen using his screening tools, asked informed questions, a first in my long relationship with the mental health system. After an extended conversation, we agreed to try an atypical antipsychotic medication, Risperidone, a medication used to treat schizophrenia, bipolar disorder, and irritability associated with autism.

I conceded that I needed to go back on lithium.

The first night on Risperidone was a horror of waking nightmares. I refused to take any more.

⁂

Early in my career, Ellie, one of my seventh-graders, thought her esophagus was a solid muscle. She saw no problem with that.

"How does your food get into your stomach?"

She rolled her eyes. "It just goes in."

"How do you throw up?"

"It just comes back up."

Oh. Things "just blended," as if a red hot dog going through a blue esophagus turned them both purple for a while, a bit like two waves passing through one another. Shifting her seventh-grade thinking was a challenge. She held the same idea about blood vessels.

"How can you bleed?"

"It just comes out."

It was difficult to argue with that.

I shared this story with Dr. Schwartz. "That's what it's been like for me. I mean one thing, and even though we use the same words, you people hear something else."

"Give me an example."

"OCD (obsessive compulsive disorder) is the easiest example. It's an anxiety disorder, right? People create rituals to feel safe.

"I have sensory issues. I like patterns which I don't want disturbed, and I'm not too fond of orange. Those are preferences, nothing to do with fear. And I'll sort anything. Jigsaw puzzles are the best, but a messy desk drawer is fun too. On the surface, it might seem like OCD, but underneath, my issue had nothing to do with anxiety. It didn't need to be addressed, much less medicated."

"The therapist who suggested I ask Dr. Grant for antidepressants also told me I had dissociative disorder. Foolish! I couldn't identify and communicate what I felt. There's a huge difference."

Dr. Schwartz was quiet. He appeared to be evaluating the information.

My heart beat wildly, filling the room with a terrifying rhythm full of calamity and fear, and I had to close my eyes to reorient myself in time and space.

This, then, was my father's secret. Autism. Of course! I was part of his pattern—every day at 7:00 p.m., he made sure I fit the American standard of beauty, 36-24-36. Making me exercise was a sore attempt at achieving an ideal which he believed would protect me. His motive wasn't sexual, although his overstimulation while coercing me to move corrupted an altogether too meddlesome behavior.

Another truth snapped into place. One of my dad's favorite expressions was: You've got rocks in your head. He meant a person was either a liar or being ridiculous. Mom had manifested an adroit parade of psychosomatic ailments through the years. For her, truth and lies ran together, blending in with each other to create hybrid truths. Dad had believed Mom's stent surgery was nothing more than another confabulation. He wasn't trying to kill her; he was trying to communicate his frustration. He used the tangible object, a two-inch rock, to scream.

It hurt to think about the magnitude of his suffering and that he'd never know what set him apart. Worse, he'd never be afforded the dignity that comes with understanding.

That recognition knit together in a split second. I shoved aside thinking about it, but a wound that had festered for fifty years healed. I forgave my father while I talked with Dr. Schwartz.

"I know you have anxiety issues."

"I do. And I'd have gotten a lot more relief if someone had taught me how to end a phone call rather than writing a prescription. Or helped me recognize sarcasm. I keep getting that one wrong."

Dr. Schwartz stretched his legs out from his chair and took off his black-framed glasses. He folded his arms over his thick girth and closed his eyes.

Not sure where I stood with him, I shared more of my history. "I swallowed antidepressants for years and years and *years*, but they didn't help. When I told Dr. Grant, she just tried different kinds. I took them like I was supposed to, but they never changed anything."

I advocated for myself for the first time. "I'm not going to experiment with more."

Dr. Westcott pointed his glasses toward me. "Trust one more time. This medication works with your dopamine system; it's different from antidepressants that target serotonin. Give your brain a chance to acclimate. I predict you won't have nightmares tonight. If I am wrong, you can have the last word."

Dr. Schwartz was right.

231

⁀

I talked with another patient, Daniel, the day before his discharge. We had traveled as isolated companions on the same road during our hospitalization. Daniel and I both had high-functioning autism and had thought death was a better alternative.

We sat at what the other patients dubbed the geek table. I told him about the angel's interpretation of E=mc^2, and we debated whether or not infinity and zero were equivalent. I was right, and if Daniel had been less familiar with theoretical mathematics, I'd have never known that. Privately, I nodded to God in whom I was starting to believe and thanked him; only an archangel could have plunked me into such company.

Daniel was young, taller than anyone on the ward, wore tinted glasses over brown eyes, and had peach fuzz for a mustache. We'd kept to ourselves and worked jigsaw puzzles in silent camaraderie.

In the patients' lounge, action movies constantly played on the television, and the rest of the crew sat for hours listening to swearing, sex, machine guns, and racing cars. Both Daniel and I wondered aloud about how such things could be allowed on the ward, rolled our eyes, and happily snapped pieces together.

I visited the sore spot first. "It's hard not fitting in."

"I've learned not to mind."

"I haven't. I just pretend like I don't."

Daniel looked at me without needing eye contact and cracked a grin. "Me too. People don't notice."

We talked about being more intelligent than most, not in a gloating manner, but rather exploring one of the traits that set us apart. I told him about the scientific research I'd encountered, feeling accomplished for the first time in many years.

Daniel talked about winning a national chess championship. He was the first person I'd met who understood the isolation of having a high IQ. Sometimes I just wanted to talk about the RNA world theory with a person who could have that conversation. It would be the kind of chatting I'd like.

I eyed the queue of chairs filled with other patients and looked at the TV. "I'd trade being smart for having that easy way with people; would you?"

Daniel snapped in a puzzle piece. "I would."

"Want to try?"

And that is how two hyposocial people found themselves watching *The Fast and the Furious* with fellow psychiatric patients who accepted us the way we were. Scarlett, the loudest, most foul-mouthed girl I'd ever met, gave up her chair to the "granny who escaped from the hippie commune," her way of being gracious.

I felt honored.

Neither the car chases that defied the laws of physics nor the gratuitous swearing mattered. We fit in for a while.

᯼

The end of my arduous journey wasn't dramatic. The frenzy that was my brain, and hence a large part of who I was, stilled under the influence of lithium and Risperidone. Lightning storms stopped rolling through my synapses. The initial sensation was akin to a Styrofoam brain being laced into a straightjacket. I sensed the high-pitched squeal as biological force gave way to a chemical one. My first impulse was to stop the medication, but then I thought about my goal. I needed the jarring emotions to be still. I, as well as family and friends, had been impotent to make that happen. It was time to accept more chemical help.

With the new medication regimen, a state of neutrality asserted itself. I could get groceries, go for a walk, or watch television without internal agony. I slept and felt like getting up in the morning.

How could two small round tablets grant such a reprieve? The miracle was too great to ponder.

Knowing I was autistic empowered me. I knew what questions to ask and what information was needed to solve problems. No longer was I a colorblind person trying to explain red. The strategies at my disposal reached far beyond distress tolerance.

I stopped thinking about suicide because the excruciating psychological pain was gone. Gone. Perhaps buying the gun was no different than stealing the salt tablets from my parents' medicine chest. I just needed a bigger bluff. There was some truth to that. But there were days that weren't about crying for help. During those hours, despair closed in, pain so raw that death seemed preferable to enduring more. My silence during those times reflected the serious danger I was in.

Was I brave enough to die? To live? This was the crux of my existential quandary. The answer had arrived in the cocoon, but I didn't recognize it. Within its altered confines, I had experienced contentment and peace, a state of mind I hadn't accessed since I was in fourth grade. Then, as now, my need to live was as present as the caterpillar's imaginal disks.

As the number of good days accumulated, I made the distinction between love and need. I'd love Joel forever, but I had fallen out of need with him. Agonizing grief sometimes rolled through, visiting for short durations of time. I wept heart-broken tears during those hours and felt a profound sense of loss. Then, the sadness ebbed into the background and I carried on.

I discovered I could be alone: the holy grail of those who suffer from borderline personality disorder.

I'd been labeled as mentally ill for so long I believed it. The distinction between being sick and being well crystallized while I was choosing grapes in the produce section of the grocery store. Suddenly, I was a well person who had become terribly ill with bipolar disorder instead of a mess who deserved to lose everything as a comeuppance. Being neurodivergent didn't mean a monster lurked within. I didn't have a deformity that needed to be fixed.

While writing, I realized the myriad guilt I carried were a different type of scar, marks so like the white traces of healing on flesh: recognizable and indelible. My actions had harmed those I loved and myself, and I would always want to make restitution. But, me, myself, and I were intact and deserved respect and kindness.

All that my family and friends asked of me was to be well, but it hadn't seemed enough of a sacrifice. The angel's message reminded me that love is simple and that the notion of needing to be in pain to apologize was absurd.

It was by sharing, I think, that I rose from shame. No matter how I reinterpreted myself as I wrote, the *me* I saw in the mirror looked wrong. I finally realized the mirror itself was broken. A shameful person began writing *In Deeper*, a different person brought it to a close.

There was more to my being than behavior, and I came to think of my actions as a second skin—a protective layer that surrounded my psyche at all times. Judgments are made about human exteriors, whether physical or behavioral, and both kinds of protective layers can be disfigured without corrupting what is within. I am certain I did the best I could and will continue to do so in the future.

In this, I trust: I am brave enough.

The days of dread are finished. My medication will protect me from my ferocious brain. Scars no longer frighten me. I release myself from the pledge I made to Joel. It is time to feel happiness, an emotion no longer connected to the pestilence of bipolar disorder. I know he'd be relieved about the broken promise.

A voice greater than I can imagine, one born of my own soul, spoke the truth. Darkness is not real.

⁂

Light is all around me.
Love is light.
Light is all there is.

A study at Baylor University found that six out of forty-one patients with borderline personality disorder fulfilled the criteria for autism spectrum condition.[10]

For decades, that person was me. No one recognized what was right under their nose.

---

10. https://www.ncbi.nlm.nih.gov/pmc/articles/PMC5590952/

Postscript

Joel and Beth reunited shortly before the publication of *In Deeper*.

About the Author

Bethany Lynne Davis is a wife, mother of two, retired teacher, and writer. She grew up in Missoula, Montana, and Fairbanks, Alaska, moving to the New England area in 1977. She now lives on the coast of Maine with her husband.

She is a summa cum laude graduate who earned a B.S. in Elementary Education in 1984 and an M.S. Ed in Exceptionality in 1990. Bethany taught grades four through eight during her twenty-seven years as a public school educator.

She presented nationally for Boston University's Microcosmos project, the G.L.O.B.E. international environmental program, and Lawrence Hall of Science.

In Deeper is her first book.